ROW, ROW, ROW

Each of these paintings in the Puzzlevania museum has something in common with the two others in the same row. For example, all the paintings in the top row across have someone wearing a gown. Look at the other rows across, down, and diagonally. What's the same about each row of three?

miss Lilli Lollipop

Answer on page 47.

MISSING PIECES

Look at each picture very carefully. Can you
guess what's missing from each item?

LIBRARY HELPERS

Sid and Sam, Joyce and Pam are library helpers. At the end of each day they push their carts through the library, gathering up all the books people have left behind. Follow each helper's trail to see how many books they collected. Who collected the most books?

Pam

Sam

Sid

Joyce

Illustrated by Anni Matsick

Answer on page 47.

DOT MAGIC

To discover who's playing this field, start at one
and connect all the dots.

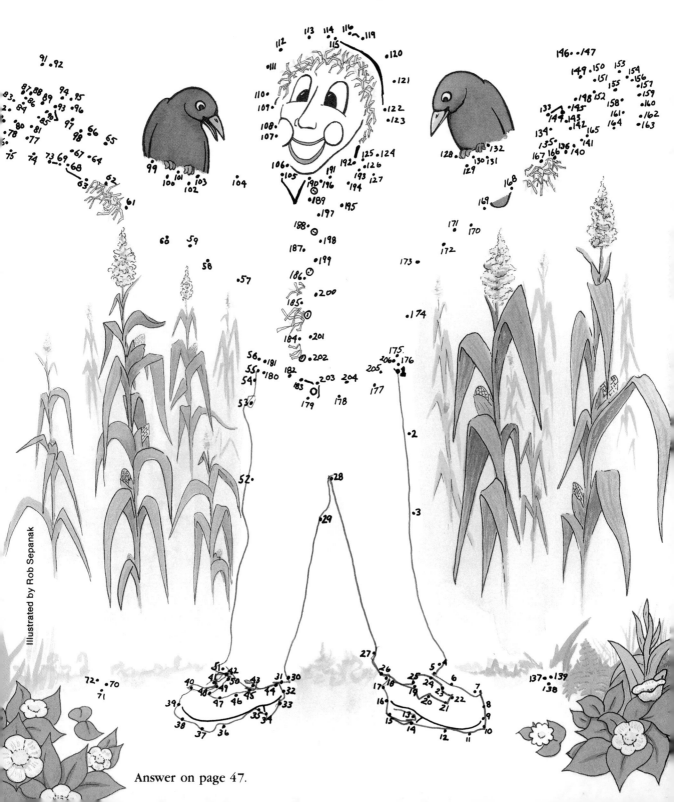

Illustrated by Rob Sepanak

Answer on page 47.

ZOO CLUES

Somebody swiped Victoria's vanilla ice cream. Track through the clues to help her find out who did it. Each clue will lead you to an animal suspect, along with some letters. The letters go into the spaces that have the same number as the clue where they were found, and may appear more than once.

Answer on page 47.

1. At the parrot tree, take the letter from the top branch.
2. The seals are balancing the next letter on their noses.
3. While the tiger is sleeping, take the letter he's guarding.
4. The polar bear is floating next to the letter you want here.
5. Maybe the elephant did it. No, he's looking for peanuts. The letter on his back is one you want twice.
6. A camel needs water, not ice cream. But you need the letter on her saddle.
7. The lion is telling the truth that he didn't do it. Take the letter from his rock.
8. Check the gorilla. He's eating a candy with double letters. Take both for your last two.

So who did it?

$\overline{3}$ $\overline{1}$ $\overline{5}$ $\quad$ $\overline{7}$ $\overline{4}$ $\overline{6}$ $\overline{2}$ $\overline{8}$ $\overline{8}$ $\overline{5}$

8

Illustrated by R. Michael Palan

HIGH JINKS

Quick, before they fall, can you follow the ropes to match each climber with their partners?

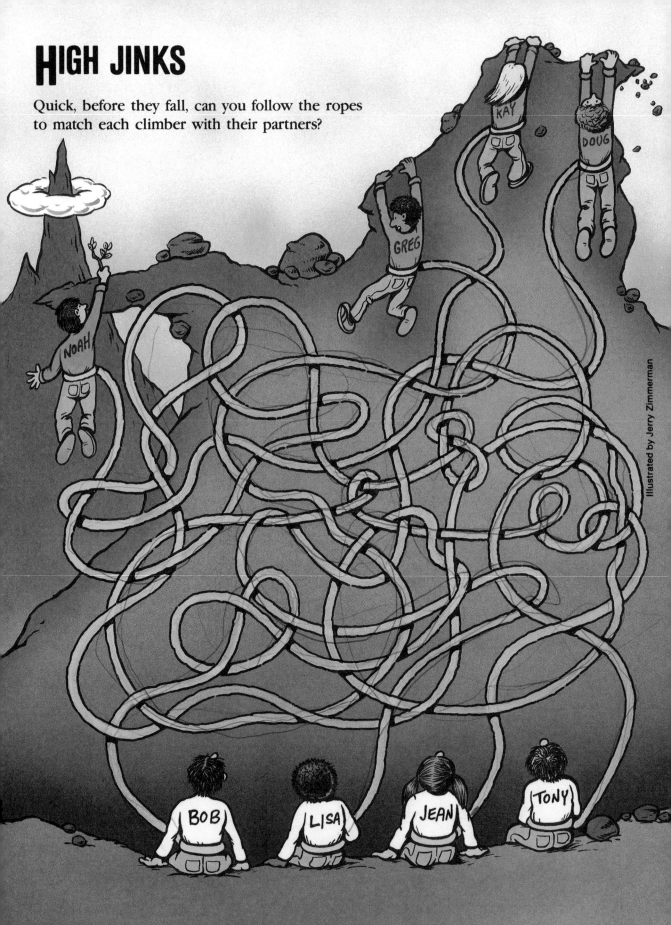

Illustrated by Jerry Zimmerman

 Answer on page 47.

STOP, LOOK, AND LIST

Under every category, list one thing that begins with each letter. For example, one unit of measurement that begins with M is Meter. See if you can name another.

UNITS OF MEASUREMENT

M _____

G _____

L _____

Q _____

S _____

ROCKS AND MINERALS

M _____

G _____

L _____

Q _____

S _____

THINGS YOU GET IN SCHOOL

M _____

G _____

L _____

Q _____

S _____

Illustrated by Lisa Dayer

Answer on page 47.

WHO SAYS?

Look at this picture and try to imagine what each person is saying. Match each sentence below with the person who might be saying it.

1. Come back with that!

2. Get away from there.

3. Brad! Good to see you.

4. Look out below!

5. Red Hots. Get your Red Hots!

6. Say, "Ah."

7. I hope I didn't miss it.

8. One, two, buckle my shoe.

9. This is supposed to be great.

Answer on page 48.

SOUND CHECK

A local band has four members (one is Sue) who play four different instruments and who like four different types of music. From the following clues can you determine each band member's favorite kind of music and the instrument that each plays?

Use the chart to keep track of your answers. Put an X in every square that can't be true, and an O in a square where the information matches. For example, clue 3 says Steve does not play the drums. So put an X in the box where Steve and drums meet.

	Guitar	Keyboards	Bass	Drums	Rock	Pop	Country	Classical
Lisa								
Sue								
Mark								
Steve								
Rock								
Pop								
Country								
Classical								

1. Lisa, who is not fond of country music, is responsible for booking all of the band's performances.
2. Although neither of the boys know how to play the keyboards, they are responsible for setting them up before each performance.
3. Steve does not play the drums, but he is an excellent songwriter.
4. The girl who likes classical (not Lisa) plays the bass.
5. The keyboard player favors pop music, but her brother (not Mark) likes rock.

Illustrated by Anni Matsick

14

Answer on page 48.

WASHED UP

Walking along the beach, you spy a bottle washed up on shore. What could be in it? A note from some navigator or a floundering flounder? A sailing ship or a stranded starfish? Use your imagination to draw what you think is in this bottle.

Illustrated by Terry Rogers

FOREIGN FUNDS

Money from all over the world is in this bank.
Can you deposit each monetary unit into the
right slot? Use the size of the words as clues,
and cross each one off the list when you find a
space for it. One country that uses each form of
money is listed in the parentheses.

2 Letters

AT (Laos)
XU (Vietnam)

3 Letters

AVO (Macao)
LEK (Albania)
LEV (Bulgaria)
ORE (Sweden)
PYA (Myanmar)
SEN (Indonesia)
WON (N. & S. Korea)
YEN (Japan)

6 Letters

BALBOA (Panama)
COLONS (Costa Rica)
DALASI (Gambia)
DIRHAM (Morocco)
DOLLAR (Australia)
FLORIN (Suriname)
GOURDE (Haiti)
HALALA (Saudi Arabia)
KOPECK (Russia)
KORUNA (Czechoslovakia)
KWANZA (Angola)
MAKUTA (Zaire)
NICKEL (USA)
PATACA (Macao)
PESETA (Spain)
SENITI (Tonga)
SHEKEL (Israel)

4 Letters

BAHT (Thailand)
BIRR (Ethiopia)
DIME (USA)
DONG (Vietnam)
INTI (Peru)
KINA (Papua New Guinea)
KOBO (Nigeria)
KYAT (Myanmar)
LIRA (Italy)
LOTI (Lesotho)
LWEI (Angola)
PARA (Yugoslavia)
PESO (Chile)
PULA (Botswana)
RIEL (Cambodia)
TALA (W. Samoa)
TOEA (Papua, New Guinea)
VATU (Vanuatu)
YUAN (China)

7 Letters

AFGHANI (Afghanistan)
BOLIVAR (Venezuela)
CRUZADO (Brazil)
DRACHMA (Greece)
EPKWELE (Equatorial Guinea)
LEMPIRA (Honduras)
QUARTER (USA)
QUETZAL (Guatemala)

5 Letters

DINAR (Kuwait)
DOBRA (Saotome)
FRANC (Djibouti)
KHOUM (Mauritania)
KRONA (Iceland)
LEONE (Sierra Leone)
LEPTA (Greece)
NAIRA (Nigeria)
NGWEE (Zambia)
PENCE (Ireland)
POUND (Egypt)
RIYAL (Qatar)
RUBLE (Russia)
RUPEE (India)
SUCRE (Ecuador)
ZLOTY (Poland)

Illustrated by John Nez

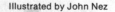

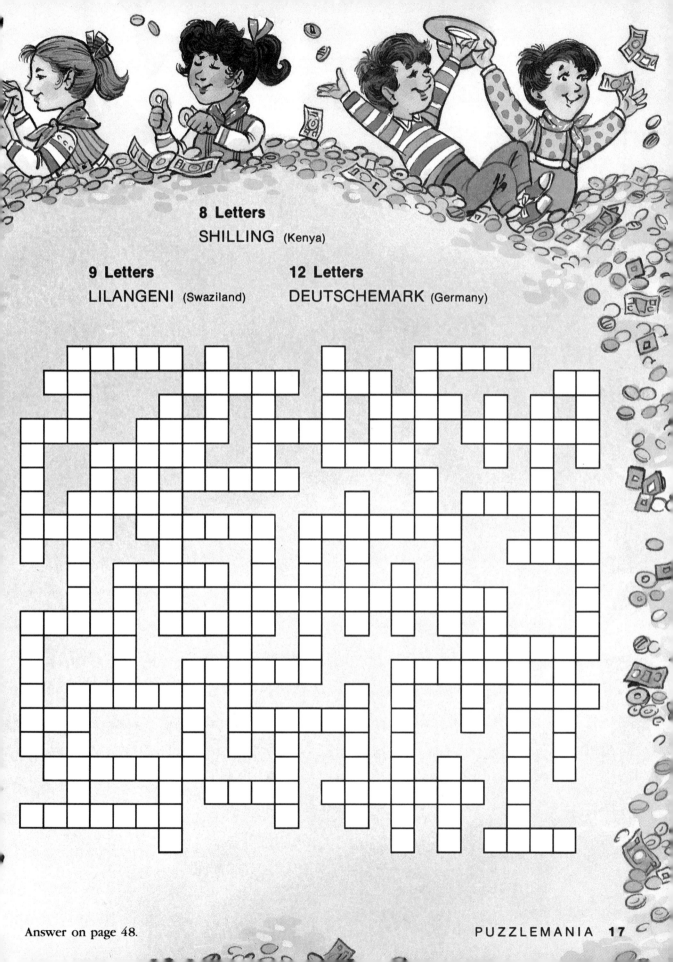

8 Letters
SHILLING (Kenya)

9 Letters
LILANGENI (Swaziland)

12 Letters
DEUTSCHEMARK (Germany)

Answer on page 48.

HIDDEN PICTURES

There are at least 22 objects hidden in this picture.
How many can you find?

POLITICAL CONNECTIONS

In politics, people sometimes find themselves grouped with very unlikely companions. In this puzzle, some very different presidents find themselves mixed into some strange groups. Using the list of the first 41 U.S. presidents and their terms of office, can you find what each group has in common? Write the names of the missing members in the blanks. To help you out, presidents are listed in chronological order.

Answer on page 48.

1. Polk, _____, Ford, Bush

2. Jefferson, Harrison, Fillmore, _____,

_____, Coolidge, Hoover, Roosevelt

_____

3. Harrison, McKinley, Taft, Wilson, _____

4. _____, Fillmore, Garfield, _____,

Kennedy, Ford

5. Washington, _____, Jackson, _____,

Grant, _____, _____,

Hoover, _____, Bush

6. Washington, Jefferson, _____, Van Buren,

Harrison, Buchanan, _____, _____,

F. Roosevelt, _____

7. J. Adams, J.Q. Adams, _____, Eisenhower

8. Monroe, Tyler, _____, Arthur, _____

20

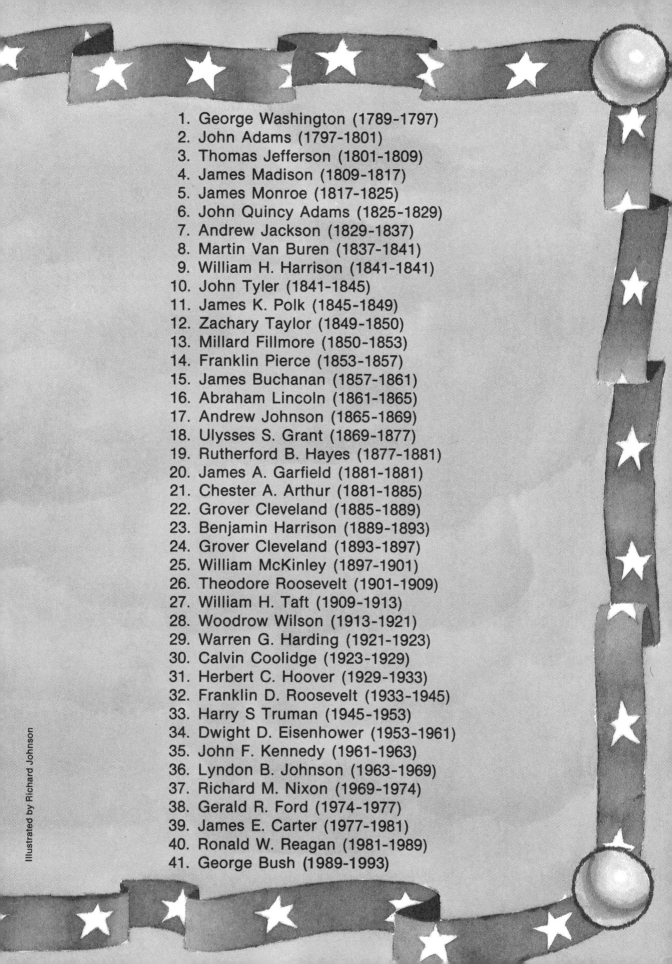

1. George Washington (1789-1797)
2. John Adams (1797-1801)
3. Thomas Jefferson (1801-1809)
4. James Madison (1809-1817)
5. James Monroe (1817-1825)
6. John Quincy Adams (1825-1829)
7. Andrew Jackson (1829-1837)
8. Martin Van Buren (1837-1841)
9. William H. Harrison (1841-1841)
10. John Tyler (1841-1845)
11. James K. Polk (1845-1849)
12. Zachary Taylor (1849-1850)
13. Millard Fillmore (1850-1853)
14. Franklin Pierce (1853-1857)
15. James Buchanan (1857-1861)
16. Abraham Lincoln (1861-1865)
17. Andrew Johnson (1865-1869)
18. Ulysses S. Grant (1869-1877)
19. Rutherford B. Hayes (1877-1881)
20. James A. Garfield (1881-1881)
21. Chester A. Arthur (1881-1885)
22. Grover Cleveland (1885-1889)
23. Benjamin Harrison (1889-1893)
24. Grover Cleveland (1893-1897)
25. William McKinley (1897-1901)
26. Theodore Roosevelt (1901-1909)
27. William H. Taft (1909-1913)
28. Woodrow Wilson (1913-1921)
29. Warren G. Harding (1921-1923)
30. Calvin Coolidge (1923-1929)
31. Herbert C. Hoover (1929-1933)
32. Franklin D. Roosevelt (1933-1945)
33. Harry S Truman (1945-1953)
34. Dwight D. Eisenhower (1953-1961)
35. John F. Kennedy (1961-1963)
36. Lyndon B. Johnson (1963-1969)
37. Richard M. Nixon (1969-1974)
38. Gerald R. Ford (1974-1977)
39. James E. Carter (1977-1981)
40. Ronald W. Reagan (1981-1989)
41. George Bush (1989-1993)

Illustrated by Richard Johnson

MOTOR MIX-UP

How many things can you find wrong in this picture?

DO RE MI

Scale new heights as you sing your way through this puzzle. Each word below contains one of the first three notes of the scale: Do, Re, or Mi. Take note of the clues to score big by filling in the missing letters to finish each word.

1. Do__: A small speck
   Re__: A color
   Mi__: To stir

2. Do__ __: Entrance
   Re__ __: True, actual
   Mi__ __: Baseball equipment

3. Do__ __ __: Giver; blood _____
   Re__ __ __: To arrive at
   Mi__ __ __: Foggy

4. Do__ __ __ __: _____ Dolittle
   Re__ __ __ __: Grooved phonograph disc
   Mi__ __ __ __: Center

5. Do__ __ __ __ __: Place to wipe your shoes before entering
   Re__ __ __ __ __: Part of song that is repeated, or to not do something
   Mi__ __ __ __ __: The least amount needed

6. Do__ __ __ __ __ __: Game using black and white tiles
   Re__ __ __ __ __ __: Telephone part or a football catcher
   Mi__ __ __ __ __ __: 12:00 p.m., the start of a new day

Answer on page 48.

PATCH MATCH

Each scout is wearing at least one patch or emblem that some other scout is also wearing. Can you find the matching patches? Not all patches will match and not all scouts will match each other.

Illustrated by R. Michael Palan

Answer on page 48.

JACK BE NIMBLE

Get a jump on all these jacks by using the clues to hammer out the answers across and down.

Across

1. Jack and the _____, a gigantic fairy tale
9. The goose laid a golden one
10. ____ Baba and the 40 Thieves
12. To stare at, rather rudely
15. A game played by players on horseback
17. The first line of a patriotic song is, "My country '____ of thee."
18. I am, You ____, He is
20. A slang word for no
21. Jack fell down and broke his _____
22. Person (abbreviation)
24. Repeated once, this is an African fly
25. Republican (abbreviation)
27. Raw minerals from which we get metal
29. Short word for miniature, like a skirt
30. What you might shout if you saw a mouse
32. A machine to make wind on a hot day
33. Another name for pancakes or griddlecakes

Down

2. Snake-like fish
3. Word for how old you are
4. No good (abbreviation)
5. Another word for good-bye is "Ta -___"
6. One of a chain of very high mountains
7. A big cat
8. When you win everything, you hit the jack___
11. A funny children's toy is a Jack-in-the-___
13. One who sends you a gift
14. He's the Jack who nips your nose and toes in winter
16. Cloth made from the flax plant
18. Paintings, photos, sculptures, etc.
19. A female sheep
22. A small, sharp noise
23. What theater film comes on, or a lively dance
25. A large circle of ice you can skate on
26. A very early spring wildflower is the Jack-in-the-pul___
28. A large body of water
29. Short for Maccabees
31. Kitchen patrol (abbreviation)
32. Fourth note of the musical scale

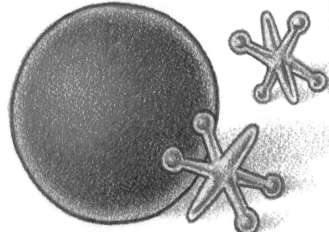

Illustrated by Gregg Valley

Answer on page 48.

CANOE CONUNDRUM

There are at least 21 canoes sailing through this picture. How many can you find?

Marc Nadel

DOTS A LOT

The answer to the riddle is hidden in the graph. Start in the first vertical column. Go from top to bottom, copying any letters where you find a dot into the blanks at the bottom. Do the same thing with all columns until the blanks are filled in and the answer is revealed.

Answer on page 48.

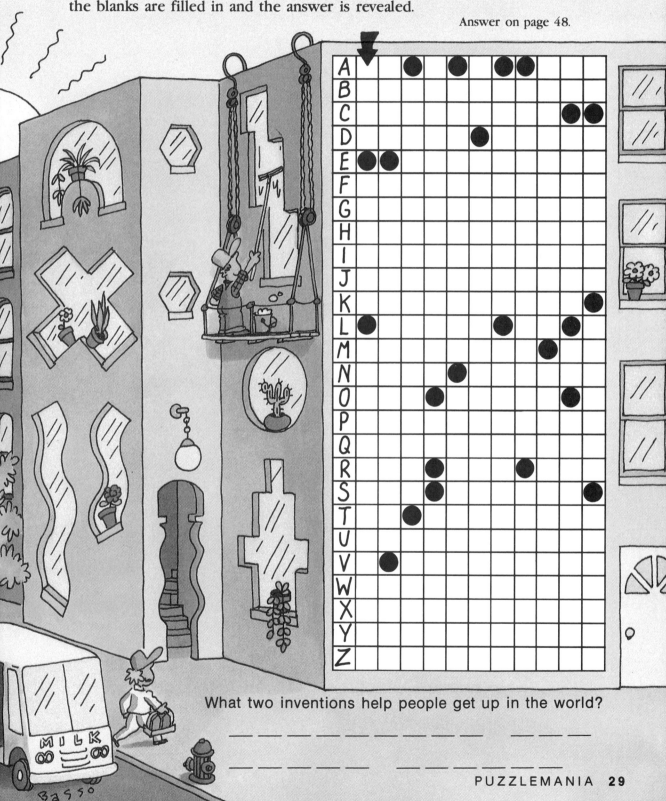

What two inventions help people get up in the world?

PICTURE MIXER

Copy these mixed-up squares in the spaces on the next page to put this picture back together. The letters and numbers tell you where each square belongs. The first one, A-3, has been done for you.

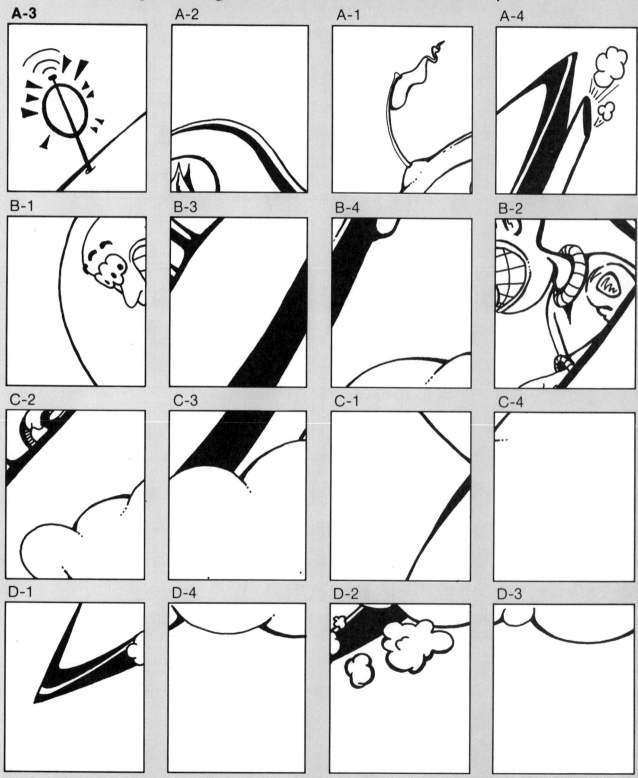

Illustrated by Rob Sepanak

	1	2	3	4
A				
B				
C				
D				

Answer on page 49.

STEER CLEAR

How many differences can you find between these two pictures?

CAMPING MEMORIES

Part 1

Take a long look at this picture. Try to remember everything you see in it. Then turn the page, and try to answer some questions about it without looking back.

Illustrated by John Nez

DON'T READ THIS UNTIL YOU HAVE LOOKED AT "Camping Memories—Part 1" ON PAGE 33

CAMPING MEMORIES   Part 2

Can you answer these questions about the camping scene you saw? Don't peek!

1. What color was the tent?
2. How many backpacks could be seen?
3. What was in the pocket of the man who was standing?
4. What was the man going to cook on the fire?
5. What plant was near the man at the campfire?
6. What was hanging from the tree?
7. How many campers wore boots?
8. What was inside the tent?
9. How many animals were in the scene?

Answer on page 49.

WHAT DOES THAT MEAN?

Can you figure out what saying is shown in each picture?

Illustrated by Gregg Valley

Answer on page 49.

WHAT'S IN A WORD?

There is a whole HERD of words hiding in the letters of DOGCATCHER.
DOG and CAT are two that are easy to spot. But how many other words
of three letters or more can you find running loose in DOGCATCHER?

DOGCATCHER

Answer on page 49.

THE CASE OF THE FIENDISH FACE

See if you can solve this mystery. Read the story and fill in the
missing words. Then match the numbered letters with the
matching spaces at the end of the story. If you fill in the
spaces correctly, you should be able to solve this case.

George was not a very happy cat. His family was taking a trip, and George

would have to stay with a neighbor. His family packed his two bowls—one for

food and the other for ___ ___ ___ ___ ___ . They prepared a basket for him to
　　　　　　　　　　　　　5　　　　　25

___ ___ ___ ___ ___ in at night and put in his favorite toys: a catnip
　　10

___ ___ ___ ___ ___ and a round rubber ___ ___ ___ ___ . Then they carried
20　　　　　　　　　　　　　　　　　　19

everything next door, including ___ ___ ___ ___ ___ ___ himself.
　　　　　　　　　　　　　　　　　　　　22

George spent the first hour hiding behind a big easy ___ ___ ___ ___ ___ and
　　　　　　　　　　　　　　　　　　　　　　　　　　　12　　　　17

the second hour glowering at Plato, the old bull___ ___ ___ who was sleeping
　　　　　　　　　　　　　　　　　　　　　　　　　　24

on a small ___ ___ ___ in front of the glowing ___ ___ ___ ___ ___ ___ ___ ___ ___ .
　　　　　　7　　　　　　　　　　　　　　　　　　2

Then, since there was ___ ___ ___ ___ ___ ___ ___ else to do, he decided to
　　　　　　　　　　　　　6　　　　　　18

explore the rest of the ___ ___ ___ ___ ___ .
　　　　　　　　　　　　　15

He padded up the ___ ___ ___ ___ ___ of a big stairway and walked down a
　　　　　　　　　　3

Illustrated by Jon Davis

long, narrow _ _ _ _ . This house was dark and a little spooky. It was
                  1

not at all friendly like George's own _ _ _ _ . All the doors except one
                                      4

were tightly closed, so George went over to peek _ _ _ _ that room.
                                                 14 16

There before him, in the dim light, he saw a scowling _ _ _ _ ,
                                                      9

with two blazing yellow _ _ _ _ . George yowled with fear. The huge
                        11

_ _ _ _ _ opened, displaying a row of sharp, white, pointed
      13

_ _ _ _ _ that gleamed through the shadows. George spun around
    8

and raced down the _ _ _ _ _ _ , his tail bristling. At the bottom
                          21

he collided with Plato, who had been awakened by the noise.

"There's a monster up there!" shrieked George, shaking with fright.

"Nonsense," growled the old dog. "Just let me check this out." Plato

lumbered up the steps, down the hall and into the _ _ _ _ .
                                                 23

In a few seconds George heard him burst out laughing.

"You didn't see any monster, you silly cat!" Plato barked.

What had George seen?   __ __ __   __ __ __
                          1 2 3   4 5 6

__ __ __ __ __ __ __ __ __ __   __ __   __
 7 8 9 10 11 12 13 14 15 16   17 18   19

__ __ __ __ __ __ .
20 21 22 23 24 25

Answer on page 49.

BLOCKBUSTERS

Look at the blocks in each row across. Can you guess which
box comes next?

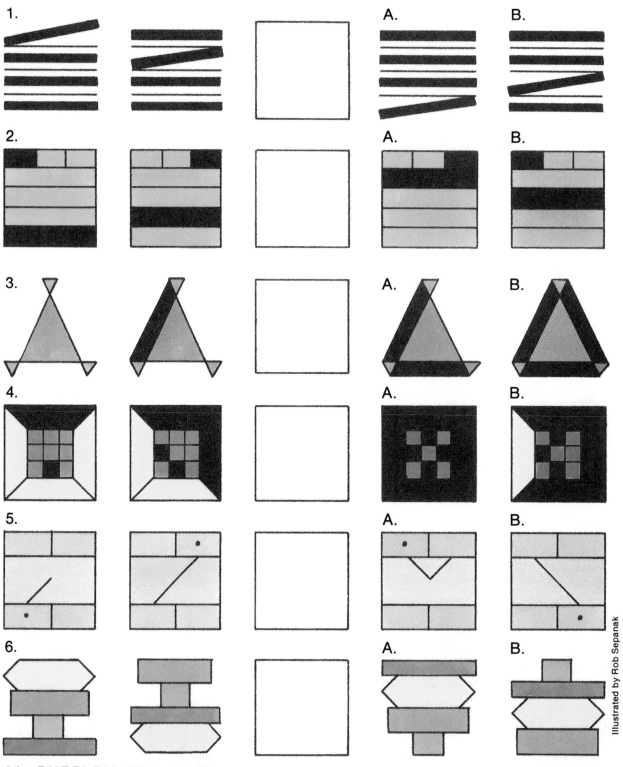

Illustrated by Rob Sepanak

Answer on page 49.

HANG ON TIGHT

This maze has its ups and downs, but see if you can find the one path from top to bottom.

Illustrated by Charles Jordan

Answer on page 49.

FIND FIVE

There are a number of words that have only five letters in them. Many are pictured on this page, like ROBIN and GOOSE. How many other five-letter words can you find, without counting plurals ending in S?

RECYCLE SCENES

Can you number these pictures to show what happened first, second, and so on?

Illustrated by Barbara Gray

Answer on page 50.

INSTANT PICTURE

To discover a great air freshener, fill in every space that contains two dots.

Illustrated by Rob Sepanak

Answer on page 50.

IN THE RUNES

While reading some old scrolls, Merlin came upon this alchemy code. It could be the key he needs to uncover the secret of the ages.

Hidden somewhere on the next scroll is every element listed in Merlin's book. Use the code to find where each element is buried. The ancient alchemists hid their secrets well, so look up, down, across, backward, and diagonally.

Illustrated by Terry Rogers

Answer on page 50.

AMBER
AQUAMARINE
BERYL
DIAMOND
EMERALD
GARNET
GOLD
JADE
LEAD
ONYX

OPAL
PEARL
PERIDOT
QUARTZ
RUBY
SAPPHIRE
SILVER
TOPAZ
TURQUOISE

SPE

TART TROUBLE

The Queen of Hearts baked some tarts to send to all her friends. But to fool the knave, she scrambled the names of fourteen famous females from fairy tales and nursery rhymes. Can you help the queen's messenger unscramble the names so he can deliver the tarts to the right women?

LETERG
LIJL
OB-EPEP
RYAM, ARYM
REDLINECLA
DOGICOLLSK
NNYEH-NYNEP
NOWS THWIE
ZARPENUL
THERMO OSEGO
TILTEL SIMS FUFTEM
DRE DRINIG ODHO
HENCKIC ILLTET
GINSPEEL TUBEAY

Answer on page 50.

Illustrated by Jon Davis

ANSWERS

COVER

ROW, ROW, ROW (page 3)

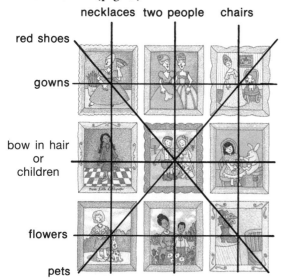

MISSING PIECES (pages 4-5)
The kite has no tail.
The computer needs a plug.
There is no eye in the needle.
This watermelon needs seeds.
The saltshaker needs holes in the top.
The turtle has no tail.
The candle needs a wick.
The envelope has no stamp.
There are no candles on the birthday cake.
There's no lace in the sneaker.
The peeler needs a hole.
The pedals are missing from the bicycle.
The butterfly needs its antennae.

LIBRARY HELPERS (page 6)
Sid   - 31
Joyce - 41
Sam   - 35
Pam   - 39
Joyce collected the most books.

DOT MAGIC (page 7)

ZOO CLUES (pages 8-9)
The Giraffe

HIGH JINKS (page 10)
Noah - Bob
Greg - Tony
Kay - Jean
Doug - Lisa

STOP, LOOK, AND LIST (page 11)
These are the answers we found. You may have
found others.

Units of Measurement	Rocks and Minerals
mile	mica
gram	granite
liter	limestone
quart	quartz
second	shale

Things You Get in School
math
grades
lunch
quizzes
spelling

WHO SAYS? (pages 12-13)

SOUND CHECK (page 14)

Sue plays the bass (clue 4) so Lisa must play the keyboards and like pop music (clue 5).

Steve likes rock (clue 5) and doesn't play the drums (clue 3) or the keyboards (clue 2) so he must play the guitar.

Mark doesn't play the keyboards (clue 2) or the bass (clue 4) so he must play drums and like country. This means that Sue must like classical.

	Guitar	Keyboards	Bass	Drums	Rock	Pop	Country	Classical
Lisa	X	O	X	X	X	O	X	X
Sue	X	X	O	X	X	X	X	O
Mark	X	X	X	O	X	X	O	X
Steve	O	X	X	X	O	X	X	X
Rock	O	X	X	X				
Pop	X	O	X	X				
Country	X	X	X	O				
Classical	X	X	O	X				

FOREIGN FUNDS (pages 16-17)

POLITICAL CONNECTIONS (pages 20-21)

1. Taft—four-letter last names
2. Harrison, Roosevelt, Kennedy—last names all contain double letters
3. Harding—first names start with "W"
4. Harrison, Harding—served less than four years
5. Madison, Taylor, Harrison, Taft, Nixon—took office in a year ending in 9
6. Madison, McKinley, T. Roosevelt, Kennedy—three-syllable last names
7. Arthur—last name starts with vowel
8. Lincoln, F. Roosevelt—left office in a year ending with 5

DO RE ME (page 23)

1. dot, red, mix
2. door, real, mitt
3. donor, reach, misty
4. doctor, record, middle
5. doormat, refrain, minimum
6. dominoes, receiver, midnight

PATCH MATCH (pages 24-25)

JACK BE NIMBLE (pages 26-27)

DOTS A LOT (page 29)

What two inventions help people get up in the world?

E L E V A T O R S   A N D
A L A R M   C L O C K S

PICTURE MIXER (pages 30-31)

CAMPING MEMORIES (page 34)
1. Yellow
2. One
3. A flashlight
4. Coffee
5. Poison ivy
6. A beehive
7. Two
8. A skunk
9. Eight—a skunk, a bear, an owl, and five bees.

WHAT DOES THAT MEAN? (page 34)
1. Jumping jacks
2. Somewhere over the rainbow
3. Rock around the clock
4. Standing in line
5. Keep it under your hat
6. It's in the bag.

WHAT'S IN A WORD? (page 35)
Here are the words we found. You may have found others.

ace	cart	credo	goad	heard	red
ache	catch	crochet	goat	heart	redo
act	catcher	crotch	go-cart	heat	retch
acted	char	dare	god	her	road
actor	charge	dart	gore	hero	rode
age	charged	date	gored	hoard	tag
aged	chart	dear	got	hod	tar
ago	cheat	dearth	grace	hog	teach
arc	chord	death	grad	hot	tear
arch	chore	dot	grade	oar	the
art	coach	dote	grate	oat	toad
ate	coat	each	great	ode	torch
cache	coated	ear	had	ore	torched
cachet	cod	earth	hag	other	tore
cad	code	eat	hard	race	trace
cadge	cog	echo	hare	rag	trade
cadre	cord	egad	hat	rat	tread
cage	core	era	hate	rate	trod
card	crag	gate	hatred	reach	
care	crate	gather	head	react	
cargo	crated	gear	hear	read	

THE CASE OF THE FIENDISH FACE (pages 36-37)

George was not a very happy cat. His family was taking a trip, and George would have to stay with a neighbor. His family packed his two bowls—one for food and the other for WATER. They prepared a basket for him to SLEEP in at night and put in his favorite toys: a catnip MOUSE and a round rubber BALL. Then they carried everything next door, including GEORGE himself.

George spent the first hour hiding behind a big easy CHAIR and the second hour glowering at Plato, the old bull DOG who was sleeping on a small RUG in front of the glowing FIREPLACE. Then, since there was NOTHING else to do, he decided to explore the rest of the HOUSE.

He padded up the STEPS of a big stairway and walked down a long, narrow HALL. This house was dark and a little spooky. It was not at all friendly like George's own HOME. All the doors except one were tightly closed, so George went over to peek INTO that room. There before him, in the dim light, he saw a scowling FACE, with two blazing yellow EYES. George yowled with fear. The huge MOUTH opened, displaying a row of sharp, pointed TEETH that gleamed through the shadows. George spun around and raced down the STAIRS, his tail bristling. At the bottom he collided with Plato, who had been awakened by the noise.

"There's a monster up there!" shrieked George, shaking with fright.

"Nonsense," growled the old dog. "Just let me check this out." Plato lumbered up the steps, down the hall and into the ROOM.

In a few seconds George heard him burst out laughing.

"You didn't see any monster, you silly cat!" Plato barked.

What had George seen?

$$\frac{H}{1} \frac{I}{2} \frac{S}{3} \quad \frac{O}{4} \frac{W}{5} \frac{N}{6} \quad \frac{R}{7} \frac{E}{8} \frac{F}{9} \frac{L}{10} \frac{E}{11} \frac{C}{12} \frac{T}{13} \frac{I}{14} \frac{O}{15} \frac{N}{16}$$

$$\frac{I}{17} \frac{N}{18} \quad \frac{A}{19} \quad \frac{M}{20} \frac{I}{21} \frac{R}{22} \frac{R}{23} \frac{O}{24} \frac{R}{25}.$$

BLOCKBUSTERS (page 38)
1. B   2. B   3. A   4. B   5. A   6. B

HANG ON TIGHT (page 39)

RECYCLE SCENES (page 42)

5   2
4   6
3   1

INSTANT PICTURE (page 43)

IN THE RUNES (pages 44-45)

TART TROUBLE (page 46)

Gretel
Jill
Bo-Peep
Mary, Mary
Cinderella
Goldilocks
Henny-Penny
Snow White
Rapunzel
Mother Goose
Little Miss Muffet
Red Riding Hood
Chicken Little
Sleeping Beauty

THE ART OF SENSUAL LOVING

This is a book to enhance your lovemaking abilities and skills. THE ART OF SENSUAL LOVING demonstrates how to do this through increasing your awareness and expression of your personal sexuality and that of your partner.

Dr Andrew Stanway's approach is to discuss sex in terms of loving and romance as much as in terms of technique – an attitude which is refreshingly welcome in today's sexual climate of concern.

Dr Stanway's wide experience as a professional therapist in the field of marital and sexual relations has revealed that many, if not most, partners today *have never really courted one another*. It is time, he claims, to return to the 'old fashioned' pleasures of courtship, intimacy and seduction; it is essential to improve our lovemaking skills in these areas if we want to ensure that we establish a committed, sexually fulfilling long-term relationship.

In THE ART OF SENSUAL LOVING, Dr Stanway reveals exactly how we can rekindle the sexual excitement within our relationships: he also devotes a section to interpreting our sexual bodies and offers intimate advice for lovemaking methods both with and without intercourse and in and out of the bedroom. The value of sex toys is discussed and much practical advice on contraception is included.

Dr Stanway's frank and informative text is perfectly complemented by sensitive and beautifully rendered illustrations in colour.

THE ART OF SENSUAL LOVING is essential reading for all those keen to learn how to both give and receive more from a loving, sexual relationship.

THE ART OF SENSUAL LOVING

A NEW APPROACH TO SEXUAL RELATIONSHIPS

DR ANDREW STANWAY

ILLUSTRATED BY JOHN GEARY

Text copyright © Andrew Stanway 1989
Illustrations copyright © Eddison Sadd Editions 1989
This edition copyright © Eddison Sadd Editions 1989

First published in the United States in 1989
by Carroll & Graf Publishers, Inc.

Tenth printing 1997

Carroll & Graf Publishers, Inc.
260 Fifth Avenue
New York, NY 10001

Library of Congress Cataloging-in-Publication Data

Stanway, Andrew.
    The art of sensual loving: a new approach to sexual relationships
    Andrew Stanway. -- 1st Carroll & Graf ed.
        p.   cm.
    Bibliography: p.
    Includes index.
    ISBN 0-88184-507-8: $15.95
        1. Sex instruction.   I. Title.
    HQ31.S77   1989
    613.9'6--dc19   89-7213
                                                          CIP

Phototypeset by Bookworm Typesetting, Manchester, England
Origination by Columbia Offset, Singapore
Printed in Hong Kong, produced by Mandarin Offset Ltd.

CONTENTS

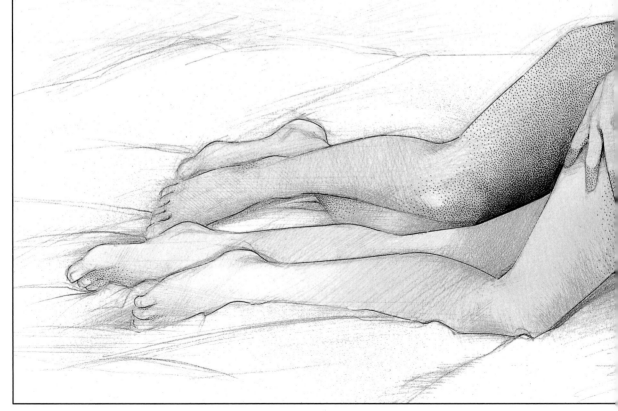

SETTING THE SCENE

MAKING LOVE WITHOUT INTERCOURSE

MAKING LOVE WITH INTERCOURSE

INTRODUCTION

Over the last thirty years there has been considerable emphasis on the physical act of lovemaking in relation to human sexual behaviour. Most of the books about sex published in the 1960s and early 1970s focused on the new-found freedoms of the time, in terms of increased sexual activity before, during and outside marriage. This, together with the introduction of the contraceptive Pill, meant that a whole generation of young people grew up to view sexual relationships in a way that was very different from that of their parents.

Today, attitudes are somewhat different again. The 'me', or more self-centred, generation is fast mellowing; concern about sexually transmitted diseases has made many people reconsider the 'anything goes' attitude towards sex and, recently, the spread of the AIDS virus has affected almost everyone's views about promiscuity.

Against this background, I sense that it is time for a book that looks at some of the non-intercourse aspects of human sexuality. To most people, sex *is* intercourse, and this is especially true for a lot of men. However, to regard sex from so narrow a viewpoint is to degrade the whole subject and to be deprived of the many lovemaking activities that have given pleasure to millions.

The ready availability of sexual intercourse during the last two or three decades has meant that many couples have run their relationships as though little else existed. Indeed, it is my experience, and that of many other therapists working in the field of marital and sexual relations, that many people today *have never really courted one another*. They dashed headlong into bed, short-cutting the loving and learning stages, only to find that once they had tasted the heady delights of intercourse, they never actually went back and learned the delicious preliminaries.

As a result, many people today become bored with their sexual relationships and start to look around to alternative partners for novelty or change. This is a terrible shame because it is probably true that for most couples, the best chance of happiness lies in the relationship they already have, rather than one which they *might* be able to make work with another partner.

With the current problems posed by an increasing variety of venereal infections, and especially with the potentially lethal

AIDS virus, we owe it to ourselves to look at how we can revive and enjoy our existing relationships, rather than to desperately search elsewhere, hoping to compensate for what we think is missing. As I have already hinted, the 'what' that we think is missing is often the ability to know and value what there is to sex other than intercourse. This is what this book is about.

In it we consider how a couple get to know one another intimately; we put sex into perspective in terms of love and romance; we learn about what our bodies respond to, and how to elicit such responses; we describe the scenes or situations most conducive to flirting, romance and love; look at methods of 'making love' without having intercourse; at how to learn more about one another at the most sensuous level; at how to make lovemaking more exciting; and much more. The last, and shortest section takes a couple into sexual activity that involves intercourse, and discusses how this should be approached in today's climate of concern.

I hope this book will be of use and pleasure to three groups of readers. Firstly, those young people who are unsure, and perhaps scared to learn about their sexuality in an age of AIDS. Many youngsters today are at a loss to know how to behave. Total sexual abstinence is clearly not an attractive proposition, yet they realize it is unwise to adopt the free sexual attitudes that perhaps their parents did. This book should help them to approach this dilemma.

Secondly, there are those couples, in their thirties and forties, who are of the 'liberated' era, and who now might be aware that there is more to sex and sexuality than their quick-to-bed past has taught them. This book will, I hope, open up new horizons for them.

Lastly, there is the older couple who probably had relatively little intercourse experience before they were married for fear of unwanted pregnancy. They, I hope, might be pleased to refresh some techniques and lovemaking skills that may have become routine, and possibly even to add new ones to enrich their middle and later years.

THE ART OF SENSUAL LOVING is, then, very different from the average 'sex book' or manual, in that it emphasizes the pleasures of non-intercourse sexuality. This is in no way meant to discourage you from sexual intercourse, but rather to enhance your abilities and lovemaking skills, and to encourage you to express your sexuality in a more varied and rewarding way. In this sense then, it is a 'how to have better sex' book. But I make no apologies for this, especially in an age when many couples are becoming only too aware that the place to look for better sex is with the partner they have. I hope this book helps you to achieve this.

CHAPTER ONE

GETTING
TO KNOW YOU

Getting to truly know someone takes a lifetime – and
even then our knowledge is far from complete. But if the
task seems daunting, it is also wonderful in the true sense
of the word, because through selfless devotion to
discovering our lover's personality, we learn so much
about ourselves and our relationship. This book is a tool
to enable lovers to know and understand one
another better.

ATTRACTION AND COURTSHIP

Although we are understandably attracted by one another's
bodies, there is far more to sexual attraction than this. Whilst
many of us start off by thinking physically, this soon changes as
we become aware of how well matched our personalities are –
the real basis for a one-to-one relationship.

Approximately ninety-five per cent of all those of marriageable age in the Western world get married at some stage in their lives, and even with the adverse press that marriage seems to be currently suffering, there is no real sign that things are changing. On the contary, even after a poor relationship, people seem to be keen to get married again.

Pair bonding, or uniting together as couples, is very much part of our culture, with most people feeling somewhat deprived if they do not have a one-to-one relationship. But what is it that brings us together in the first place?

Studies with specially designed eye cameras that tell an observer exactly what a person is looking at, even if only for a split second, reveal that we make decisions very quickly indeed, about the appearance of the opposite sex. Within seconds we have visually summed up a person and decided, usually quite unconsciously, whether or not they are worth taking further.

Body shape and style, clothes, height, body odour, the face, and many other factors, all play their part in helping us decide whether someone is likely to be sexually attractive.

Just why any one, or a combination of, these facts should be important to any particular individual is not known, but there are thousands of learned papers on this subject to be found in psychology journals. Perhaps we unconsciously go for people who are somehow like our parents, on the basis that they are familiar in highly specific anatomical ways; perhaps we select those who have features that are generally accepted to be attractive in individuals of the opposite sex; or perhaps looks are not nearly as important as we imagine them to be and other non-physical factors are in operation. In many ways the attraction of one person for another is a total mystery and defies even scrupulous study.

Obviously, we cannot get to know everybody we ever meet and as a result we become rather skilled at sorting out those who might be suitable for us to mate with. From a fairly small selection – few of us have that much choice when the matter is looked into in some depth – we then summon our unconscious notions of attractiveness, acquired over our lifetime thus far. For instance, when we see an outgoing woman with long fingernails and dyed red hair, or a man with a chunky gold bracelet, we make immediate assumptions about her

There is a lot more going on here than the exchange of bodily
sensations. Holding hands says 'We are one'.

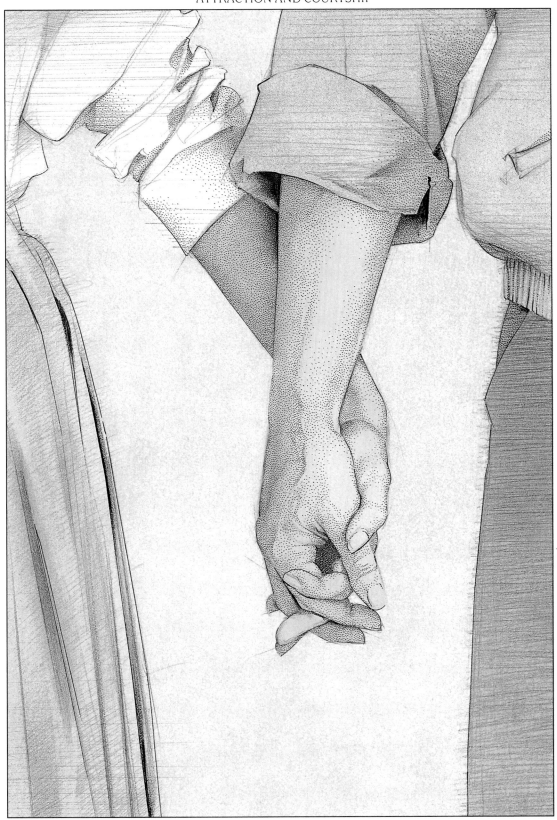

or his personality based on our previous experience or that of our trusted contemporaries. This reliance on judgements made using stereotypes can be dangerous but it is generally the only practical way.

Now the real business of establishing a one-to-one relationship begins. We start the process of finding out about the person, to see if they are the sort of individual with whom we might have something in common.

Similarity then, and the possibility of taking things further, is the first basis for selection because we all need a core of common interests if we are to be happy together for any length of time. I always tell couples that the best partner for most of us is one who has enough in common with us so that we do not have to redefine our interests every ten minutes and yet who has enough difference to make them stimulating and to open up new horizons for us.

This balance between what we know and are at ease with and the thrill of the new is what can make partner selection so difficult. There is good evidence that almost any man and any women of fairly similar backgrounds *could* be good partners for one another. Having said this, there are certain guidelines that should be considered when choosing someone for life. Rushing into a relationship; an over-emphasis on romance; relying too much on looks; too restricted a choice; and looking to sex too early; all probably exert negative effects on making rational choices. This is a pity because they can all be controlled, thereby saving the possibility of heartache later.

Courtship becomes the most important thing that any couple ever embark on. During the slow, stepwise revelation of one another's personality we learn about how we truly are in the presence of our partner and how they are with us. Courtship is a time of appraisal, approach and approval. It is a testing stage, and if properly used, will sow the seeds for romantic, loving and realistic behaviour for a whole lifetime together. Far too many young people rush into sexual activities before they have really got to know one another. This has probably always been the case to some extent, but given that 'Til death us do part' is now an average of fifty-two years for the young couple marrying today, the more homework they do before they actually tie the knot the better.

Couples who cut short their courtship tell me that they find it almost impossible to compensate later. Indeed, one of my tasks as a marital therapist is to teach people, often in their forties, or older, how to court one another. They progressed headlong from friendship and physical attraction to bed and as a result cut short any other sort of discovery about one another. Sex is often such a powerful drive that few of us can ignore the feelings and make a rational judgement about other less satisfactory areas of our new partner's personality or suitability for a life together.

But going back to courtship after many years together can be hard to do. After all, over the years many people become lazy and tend to take their partner for granted. The essence of courtship behaviour is that we are really trying; really putting ourselves out for our partner and delighted to be doing so. In short, we are on our best behaviour when we are courting, trying to encourage the other person to think well of us.

What makes returning to courtship behaviour so difficult for many is that they have all but forgotten how to be enthusiastic about each other. Things have become sloppy; manners in and out of bed may be poor; assumptions are made that are often harmful and erroneous; minds are closed rather than open; and the past is focussed upon rather than the future. To the courting couple, the present is important and so is their anticipation of the future. Most couples I see who do not court one another in later life no longer have an eager and excited anticipation of what the future holds because they wrongly assume that they know.

I say 'wrongly' because although they *can* live out their present model for the rest of their lives together, there are in fact other possibilities every bit as exciting and unknown as the future for the couple who are courting at the beginning of a relationship. The couple who continue courting one another throughout their marriage together make no assumptions about life being the same, possibly boring, script that they have been acting out thus far. They see courtship behaviour as a re-dedication to one another; a sign that they have a future which involves change and the excitement of the unknown; and that life's script, whilst valid for where they are, can change as *they* change as individuals and as a couple.

As the Agony Uncle for a wedding magazine, I get letters from many people about to get married. The most common theme of these letters is that a woman is concerned about her fiancé in some way and is wondering whether he will change after marriage. Usually the letter assures me that, contrary to what everybody says, she is sure that she will be able to change him.

I also write another similar column for a women's magazine. Similar letters here, and my own clinical experience, show me that these women are indulging in wishful thinking or even arrogance. Most men stay much as they are, at least in fundamental ways, and the woman who thinks that she can substantially change her partner after marriage is usually in for a rude shock.

This emphasizes my view that we should take our time getting to know one another, warts and all, during courtship. This, to me, means a slow progress towards sex, perhaps taking some months, living together as much as possible, though not necessarily under the same roof, so that we see each other as realistically as possible, and not just acting a part. There should be no game playing – at least not consciously so, during courtship – it is a time for frank revelations.

When sex does start to become a part of the relationship, progress should again be slow. I find that the couple who share everything gently and lovingly stand a much better chance of happiness early on in marriage, let alone later. When people who are getting divorced are asked when they first knew the relationship was wrong many say, 'In the first year, or even sooner'. Much mismatching would be avoided if couples went about their courtship gently and honestly and abandoned the relationship if their partner was unsuitable.

Sharing fantasies, playing romantic games, and learning what really excites one another, are just a part of the whole revelatory process that is at the heart of real courtship.

None of us can know for sure that we are making the right choice when selecting a lifetime partner and there are no guarantees handed out at any wedding ceremony. With care and honesty though, we can be reasonably sure before we marry that there is suffficient in common and yet enough difference to remain interesting, so that we do not receive any dramatic surprises early on in our marriage.

With this kind of goodwill, understanding and trust established early on, most couples can then face the inevitable changes that occur in life. A well-founded, realistically based sexual life together also helps when the pressures of life intrude. People are always asking me what could be done to make marriage more successful. There are many possible answers but if I had to choose just one, it would be to institute premarriage courses in courtship. If we all started a marriage with a 'degree' in courtship there would be fewer divorces and many happier and fulfilled couples.

Tenderness is highly attractive in a man. In fact, the combination of strength, both emotional and physical, with tenderness, is an irresistible combination.

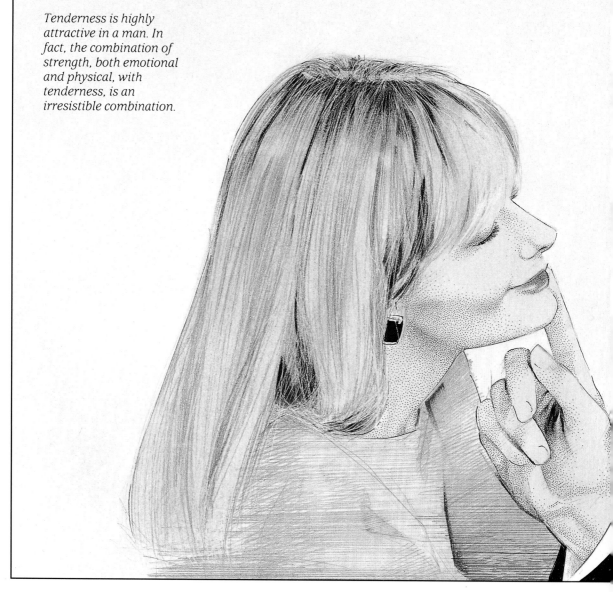

THE ART OF SEDUCTION

*Seduction can take place as a part of courtship; as an activity in
its own right, for a couple who fancy one another; or can be a
part of the daily lives of a couple that are already lovers.
Although it might appear that the game would be different in
each situation, in fact there are many more similarities than
one would expect.*

Sex is a powerful force in our lives and one which we are all obliged to deal
with. However, unlike going to a restaurant for a meal, the sexual appetite is
not so easily satisfied. It requires playing a fairly sophisticated game with
someone of the opposite sex, either as a part of courtship or an existing
one-to-one relationship.

The goal of seduction is to have intercourse with the other person. This goal
might not be the conscious agenda between two people, but even if it is an
unconscious one when seduction occurs, sex will usually be the outcome.
Unconscious agendas are often at the heart of an affair and can prove to be a
marriage breaker. How much better then, to recognize seduction when you see
it, either in yourself or others, so that if it is not what you want, or it could
jeopardize your one-to-one relationship, you can bring it to an end before you
become hopelessly involved.

Having sex with someone new is not simply a matter of asking for it outright.
There is a series of culturally accepted stages we all work through, if only
unconsciously. Firstly, we select an available partner; next, we develop their
interest in us; we then sustain their interest; move on to introduce the subject
of sex; and lastly have sex.

The way in which we seek out a new partner is important. For some people
the main thrill is to be found in the chase. Once they obtain the object of their
desire they quickly cool off. Such people are often somewhat unsure of
themselves and once they have proved that they *can* attract someone of the
opposite sex, they retreat, to try it all over again on the basis that 'one piece of
evidence doesn't actually prove anything'. Others back off because of their
conscious, or unconscious, inhibitions about the opposite sex. From another
point of view there are those who love to *be* chased, and never want to take it
further. They too have problems with their personal opinion of their
acceptability, or even possibly the acceptability of others.

There is good evidence that we all have a reasonably good idea of how
attractive we are. Unconsciously then, we seek out someone who we feel is in
our league of attractiveness. In this way, we do not waste time with someone
who is much more attractive than ourselves, in case they reject us. It is
interesting that research reveals that people do indeed marry a person of an
approximately comparable attractiveness rating, as judged by others.

Choosing the person to seduce is only the start; we next have to select the
right moment to approach them with our desire. This can be much more

difficult. Your chances of successfully seducing someone are greater if you are careful to be particular about the situation. Rewards can be expected where there is heightened emotional arousal. People have been found to fall in love more readily after natural disasters and tragedies, but I am not suggesting that you wait for or create one of these! You could settle for meeting at a dance, a sports centre, pop concert, a religious meeting, or 'dangerous' situations such as fairgrounds. Excitement and some danger, compounded by a shared enjoyment of the surroundings, make people more likely to be open to one another's advances. It could be that the adrenaline, the relative loss of inhibitions, and the sheer power of the shared experience make people feel closer together and so more open to being seduced.

Shared experiences that have a special meaning for the individuals concerned are common situations for seduction to take place. This is why so many people find themselves seducing and being seduced on courses of all kinds; on training days; where they are overcoming a common foe or sharing a common emotion. Danger, or even the threat of it, according to studies, seems to make men especially, more amorous.

The next consideration is whether the person you have decided to pursue is likely to respond to your approach. For instance, studies show that women who smoke are more promiscuous than women who do not. There are numerous other stereotypical findings that we use, however unconsciously. Body language can betray many of our feelings and is almost impossible to disguise, even if we want to. 'Open postures', those that display ourselves, are clear indications that we are available to the right person. Looking at someone just that little bit too long; actually gazing into someone's eyes; laughing at their jokes; these are just a few of the ways through which it becomes apparent that a welcome response might be possible.

So it is that we decide whether someone is available; whether they are attractive enough to pursue further; how good a match they would make; and whether they appear to be interested in us. Much of this evidence is obtained on a highly subjective basis but we have to start somewhere.

The next phase of seduction is to declare things about yourself in order to make you appear normal, attractive, healthy, and likely to be a good partner. This involves what is called self-disclosure. Apart from saying that you work in a bank, or whatever, much more is required for things to progress. Emotional and psychological disclosure seems to be most successful. This makes the other person feel that you are mature, open, honest and likely to be pleasant to deal with sexually. It is interesting that these kinds of disclosures by someone who is married, to another who is trying to seduce them, are almost certain to start an affair. Research has found that married people who disclose information about their emotions and personal lives to others of the opposite sex are much more likely to get divorced than those who do not.

Usually men take the lead in this exposure of their emotions but women soon join in and true communication begins. Enabling or encouraging another person to disclose information in this way, is all part of being a successful seducer. Indeed, a lot of 'chatting up' involves skilful, subtle, encouragement to someone to reveal more about themselves than perhaps they ideally would like. This is especially true for affairs. Most people in this situation present a very good face to the individual they are seducing. They are keenly interested in what is being said, for example. This is one of the reasons why the one being seduced is often so taken with the seducer – he or she is too good to be true.

By making some snap judgements about early developments you can now work on sustaining the other person's interest in you. Now is the time to be especially sensitive to the signs of rejection. Of course, things can go the other way, with someone you thought did not care, suddenly starting to be keen. Find an interesting topic of conversation and develop it with some fervour. In addition to this, be sure to listen attentively. Most people like talking about themselves and a good listener is highly prized.

As matters progress – and they do so rather slowly in humans – employ flirtation to show that you are interested not only in the individual's mind but in their body as well. This, if subtly done, keeps the possibility of sex open while you each feel your way in other dimensions of the relationship.

Playing hard to get or seeming to be unavailable, is a common game used unconsciously and consciously by both sexes. Too readily available a partner puts many people off, especially today as promiscuity becomes increasingly unfashionable, but the opposite is equally annoying. Research has found that men fear rejection early on, especially by attractive partners, so anything a woman can do to reassure the man that this is not likely to occur will maintain progress and ensure that he remains happy. A woman who wants a man must show that she is 'gettable' or he will leave her for someone who is. Both men and women enjoy the chase but will abandon a chase they are not likely to win.

Our culture teaches that women and girls should not appear too easy to seduce but this is a difficult position to establish because they must not scare men off completely. I advise women to be open about their sexuality so that men know what the situation is right from the start. If they are attracted to the man it makes sense to go for him and not to play games. If they do not feel attracted, or they are married and do not want to tempt fate, they should stop things immediately and allow him to look elsewhere.

By now sexual arousal is usually becoming a part of the game. Establish that you are desirable and available, but that you would also like to be wooed. This is true for either sex.

In our culture we do not go up to someone and ask for sex outright. We talk about it first in the abstract and avoid direct reference for a while, testing the temperature of the water before jumping in. As this kind of talk progresses it becomes apparent whether it will be possible to reach the level of intimacy required for sex. The very ambiguity of this indirect approach means that rejection is less painful because the advance was so tentative and oblique. Rejection at this stage involves very little loss of self-esteem but if you have received the right messages things can, and will, proceed. At this stage, we probably obtain

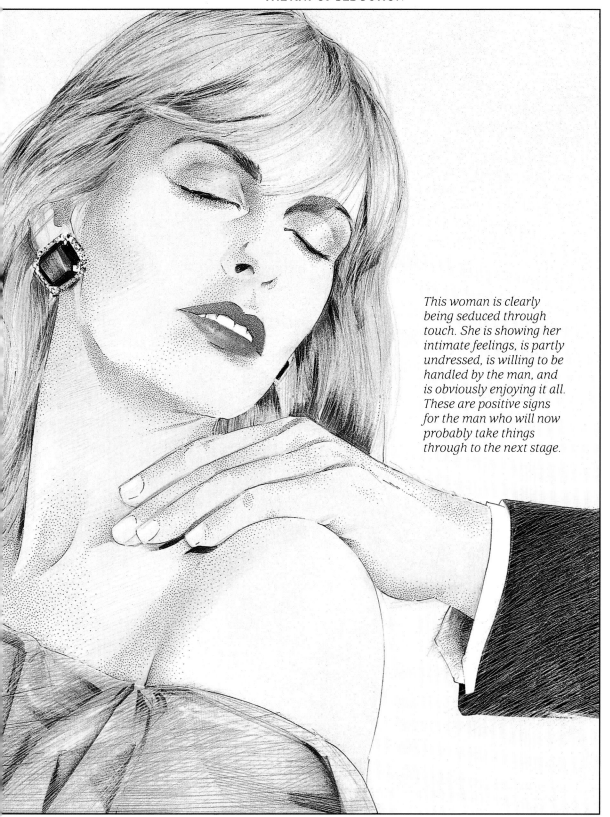

This woman is clearly being seduced through touch. She is showing her intimate feelings, is partly undressed, is willing to be handled by the man, and is obviously enjoying it all. These are positive signs for the man who will now probably take things through to the next stage.

about eighty per cent of our information from body language so practice being more aware of this, rather than of what the person says.

Verbal cues should soon start to be positive as well. This, together with more intimate discussion of sex, contraception, the future and so on, all signal the readiness of a couple for sex. At this stage, if not before, the other person starts to do us favours, to put themselves out for us, perhaps to deceive their partners for us, or to shun other members of the opposite sex. This builds the relationship further and makes each person more valuable to the other. Now physical activities reach the point where intercourse occurs.

After the first time that this happens, most people talk about how it was for them; how much they feel for one another; women usually protest some sort of love for the man, if only to assuage their guilt, if they are guilty, and many are; make plans for doing it again; and discuss their future together even if at this stage it seems likely to be short-term.

From here on the couple start to build a sexual and romantic life together and can be said to have a 'history'. Slowly, perhaps over some months, they use their knowledge to seduce one another increasingly well until they become experienced lovers. This is also a behaviour that is open to people who have been married for many years. When I talk to married couples about seducing one another they often look at me as if I were mad, thinking that only the unmarried or those having affairs, seduce one another. But this is not so. A really successful couple are still delighting one another by seducing each other year after year. This can, in fact, be highly rewarding if only because as long-term partners we know so much about one another.

It is a pity that so many couples seem to find the idea of seducing one another rather odd. As I have pointed out, this is a shame because it is often the perceived 'unseducibility' of our partner that makes them appear dull or less interesting than other members of the opposite sex. My clinical experience shows me that few couples continue to make the investment they could in seducing one another on an ongoing basis, mainly because they believe that once you have secured a partner you no longer need to seduce them – everything should then automatically be available without any fuss or effort.

This, unfortunately, misses much of the point of sexual pleasure. Anticipation is half the joy and the chase often more stimulating than the catch. By reducing the art of seduction in a long-term relationship we miss out on a lot of fun, anticipation and excitement.

Some good advice for couples of any age or at any stage in a relationship is to make a conscious effort to plan seducing one another frequently. None of us likes to be taken for granted. Knowing that you are going to both seduce and be seduced in your relationship not only keeps you feeling young as you re-live the exciting stages of late adolescence together, but also makes you feel valuable to your partner and keeps you alert to any possible hints of a serious danger of your love life becoming routine.

When people are asked why they have affairs they list many reasons. But for most people an affair is a secret adventure to add fun and excitement to their lacklustre sexual and romantic lives. The couple who seduce one another frequently have no such problems because they can create similar adventures with their partner – and without all the disadvantages of having to anticipate or learn about the desires of someone new.

But whether you are married or not, it makes sense to put some effort into studying just how you would seduce someone – what produces the best results, and what does not. Consider your style; look carefully at which ploys work best; which locations seem to please your partner best; or if you are at the stage of seeking a partner, what kinds of seduction work best to attract the kind of person you really want.

This can be a complicated process if we are inexperienced in the art of seduction, as we have everything to learn and because what we think we *want* and what we actually *need* can be two rather different things. The trouble is that when we are young we find it difficult, if not impossible, to separate the two desires. This can make it hard for us to seduce the sort of person we think we want because our personality structure simply prevents us from producing what we think are the best results. This leads some people to suffer endless frustration and heartache as they find it hard to attract and seduce the partners they think they want. Sometimes talking this over with a really good friend can help. Even a loving parent can give the odd tip or piece of advice that can help you decide who you need. Quite a lot of people waste time with seduction ploys that will not attract or keep the sort of individual they need, yet they seem unable to change their tactics.

As we get older and more experienced most of us come to understand what it is that we really *need* in a partner and are, as a result, much more realistic about how to set about seducing the appropriate person. This learning can also be applied to our one-to-one relationship so as to achieve the best results.

Seducing someone we know extremely well can be delicious *because* of its predictability. After all, sex with someone new presents all kinds of pitfalls. Will I satisfy him/her? Will I be as good as his/her other partners? Will I come too soon/too late? Will I come at all? What about my fat tummy? These quite understandable fears are all insignificant in the long-term, trusting relationship because such a couple know about one another's needs and value even the apparently unattractive things about each other. This predictability is a tremendous force for good in a stable relationship. As a culture we tend to have become carried away with the novel and different. By this token a partner who has been with you for ten years all too easily becomes 'a bore'. This is a terrible waste and in the light of current concern about AIDS, is also somewhat unwise.

When people come to me complaining about their 'impossible' partner I point out that the partner we have is usually the best, unless there is very obvious evidence to the contrary. Most people do best putting more of an investment into their existing relationship than starting again with someone else. If only most people about to break up their relationship realized the amount of effort that goes in to starting all over again I am sure that they would try harder to make their current relationship work.

Doing this involves seducing one another frequently; expertly; uniquely; and enthusiastically. The couple that do this keep romance alive; are never bored; go from strength to strength; and build a partnership that is unassailable from the outside.

IT'S ALL IN THE MIND

*Humans are such cerebral animals that it is hardly surprising
that sometimes sex appears to be more of a mental activity than
a physical one. The mind is probably our most important sex
organ, followed by the skin. By comparison, the genitals
come a poor third.*

We all have a capacity for imagination and fantasy. From babyhood, fantasies and daydreams play a vital role in our lives. Our earliest games involve playing 'make believe'. Of course, most people fantasize about all sorts of subjects – not just sex. We think in a similar way about holidays, a new car, our children, and so on. Living *totally* within the boundaries of reality is probably unacceptable to most people, and it does seem as if we need some form of safety valve to enable us to escape from the real world.

Almost everybody has sexual fantasies, if only from time to time. They are normal, are not necessarily unfulfilled wishes or desires, nor are they necessarily a symptom of problems in a relationship. Sexual fantasies can take the form of repeated, compulsive talismans that are essential for sexual success; they may be fleeting daydreams; nocturnal episodes that accompany wet dreams; or memories of previous erotic encounters. On occasions they take the place of reality when an activity would be unacceptable or unavailable in real life. Many women, for example, have fantasies about being taken roughly or even 'raped' if only by someone they love. In true life they would be absolutely horrified, but in fantasy it is fun, arousing, and acceptable to them.

People frequently use fantasies when masturbating. They thereby quite consciously control both the body and the psyche and so make the experience as pleasurable as possible. This is why masturbation is often reported as being so exciting compared with intercourse. Everything can be made perfect.

For some people intercourse itself is impossible without some sort of fantasy, however fleeting. This is a perfectly acceptable way of compensating in the mind for deficits in the real-life partner we have. For some people this is the only way that they can cope with sex at all; for example, the married homosexual man or woman who wants to stay married, or the individual with an unacceptable 'perversion' that can be contained only in fantasy.

The secret of the success of fantasies is that our fantasy partners are perfectly suited to our unconscious because, of course, they are the creation of it. They are always attractive to us, are sexually able and enthusiastic, and never complain of a headache. In short, they are idealized. Using such partners we can compensate for any deficits in our own lives or even rehearse what is about to happen in our relationship.

*This couple have just started a physical sexual encounter. Perhaps one
of them has even rehearsed in fantasy exactly what will happen next.*

There are as many actual fantasies as there are individuals but having said this, there are certain commonly recurring themes that are favourites for many people. Making love out-of-doors or in romantic settings; making love with our partner, or being kissed passionately, masturbated, or having oral sex with them; are all popular. More adventurous fantasies are also extremely common. These include wild orgies, wife-swapping, and same-sex fantasies.

About half of all fantasies involve personal romantic and loving episodes from the past, if surveys are to be believed. Exploratory, or 'way out' ones are the next most common. Whilst it is an over-simplification to claim that women are more 'masochistic' than are men, it is true that more men have fantasies involving control and active behaviour whereas women have more fantasies that involve 'being done to'. Of course, there is a considerable overlap, as with everything to do with the sexes. Indeed, many men say in therapy sessions that they wish their partner would realize that they like having things done *to* them and that they do not want to be 'in charge' all the time.

What then, are the commonest fantasies? In males, group sex, even if this only amounts to being made love to by two women, is always near the top of the list. The second most popular area concerns voyeuristic pastimes such as looking at a woman in stockings and suspenders; women engaging in particularly provocative activities, such as stripping or dancing erotically and so on. Of the sexes, men seem to monopolize fetishistic fantasies that involve key objects as almost magical sexual talismans. This sort of fantasy is occurring increasingly in women as they become more liberal-minded about sex.

Women predominately fantasize about a loved partner; with sex in romantic and exotic settings coming a close second. Reliving a past encounter with a special person is highly popular. Rape, near-rape or a fantasy involving some sort of physical force always occurs high on the list in all research into female fantasy. Having sex with animals is surprisingly common too.

It appears from studies, that men generally have more sexual fantasies than do women. Whether such studies reflect the truth is open to doubt. If men are not having sex, they still fantasize quite a lot but when placed in extreme situations, such as in prisons, their ability to fantasize is lessened.

The trend when women are surveyed appears to be rather different. Most women say that they do not fantasize much if they are not having regular sex but that if they are, they fantasize a great deal. A rich fantasy life in a woman is usually a reflection of her general activity, wellbeing and creativity rather than any dissatisfaction with her partner. some men misunderstand this and are terribly hurt when their partner declares her rich fantasy life. A sensitive man sees it rather differently because he knows that her high level of fantasy is reflected in and enriches their relationship.

How can a couple use their fantasies to enhance and protect their lives together?

• An individual can rehearse in fantasy something he or she is planning to do, or wants to do, within the relationship. This not only enhances the pleasure when the real event occurs but helps to resolve any practical details so that the adventure is successful on the day.

• Fantasies can be used to accommodate sexual and erotic needs in a harmless way during masturbation if the individual knows that their partner cannot accede to their wishes.

● Fantasies can be invaluable to aid arousal or even sometimes to produce arousal when other environmental factors are working against the individual. A recently unemployed man, a mother who has had little sleep, a couple who are worried about money, or whatever, can, by using fantasies either in their own mind, or sharing them (see page 80) overcome even quite considerable 'anti-performance' odds and have an enjoyable and fulfilling sexual encounter.

● By actively feeding the fantasies of our partner we can help him or her to get more pleasure from sex. This 'whisper in your ear' game can transform a sexual encounter that is failing, into a tremendous success within minutes.

● The need to fulfil unusual or 'odd' sexual needs can be coped with in fantasy, whether or not your partner wants to be involved. For instance, some things, such as same-sex desires, cannot be dealt with by a partner, even if he or she wanted to.

● Fantasy can be used as an aid to masturbation to heighten the enjoyment. The value of masturbation cannot be overestimated in any loving relationship so anything that enhances it is helpful.

● By fantasizing about someone of the same or the opposite sex it is possible to defuse your lust for them without dealing with them personally and thereby endangering your one-to-one relationship.

● In fantasy we can relive old romantic episodes either with our current partner or a previous one almost in the same way we look back at photograph albums with pleasure.

● Fantasy can also be used as a form of auto-hypnotic method at times of boredom or stress. Some of my patients practice this expertly. They use their favourite fantasy when at the dentist, when travelling to an examination or other stressful event, when sitting for long periods on a bus or delayed train, and so on.

● And lastly by sharing fantasies we have the opportunity to enrich our love lives together in a way that brings us closer, makes us truly intimate, and strengthens the bond between us.

CHAPTER TWO

MAKING A COMMITMENT

As we slowly explore and enjoy each other's personality
we feel happy and encouraged to take things further.
This, over some weeks or months, leads to a serious
commitment to one another – to creating a bond that
says 'You are special to me and worth investing in on
a one-to-one basis'.

DISCOVERING INTIMACY

Intimacy is a difficult concept for many people to grasp – indeed it can mean different things even within any one relationship – so it is hardly surprising that couples find it hard to understand, or even to discuss. To some it means closeness, to others physical affection, and to yet others a sort of soul-to-soul sharing. Whichever way you see it, it is vital in a loving relationship.

If we are to understand intimacy in any true sense we have first to look at the concept of personal space. This involves not only physical space but also emotional, spiritual and psychological space. We all need to have our own personal space in which to be ourselves, even, or perhaps especially, if we are pair-bonded with a lifetime partner. We are not our partner and never will be and however *close* we are we may never be truly *intimate*. Indeed, over-closeness is the enemy of true intimacy, as we shall see.

Modern life involves being together with people much of the time, whether at home in our one-to-one relationship or at work or play. Of course, we are social animals and need one another's company but all too often we can find ourselves leading a life that is centred around others or even living for them. At this end of the scale are those who feel valid only if they are being of service to others. They have no 'right' being themselves, or so they think, and as a result often do not really know who they are. At the other extreme are those who are so self-centred that they *cannot* relate to others. Somewhere between these two points is where most of us need to be to lead a healthy and fulfilling life.

Personal space is more of an inner concept than a physical one. It is possible to experience it in a crowded room or on a train full of people. This is because it has little to do with the presence of others and everything to do with our view of ourselves. An individual who is at peace with him or herself can revel in their personal space and value it.

If we are mothered well we learn as a baby to value ourselves. A good mother helps her child feel good about itself, to feel cherished and loved, not because of what the child does or does not do but simply because it is who it is. This so-called unconditional love makes people grow up to feel happy and worthy of a personal space. If I unconditionally love my partner I allow her to be fully herself – not something I need her to be if she is to answer *my* needs. The experience of being loved is all about being fully oneself, not about being what others think of us or need us to be.

It is my experience, and that of most people working in this field, that most emotional problems in childhood arise from poor loving. Children who are loved on condition that they become as their parents wish, grow up to find difficulties with the concept of personal space. Early in life we learn to trust, and to be afraid of being separated from our care-giving mother. But this very placing of trust in others makes us vulnerable to being let down and hurt by those who love us. This is, alas, a part of the gamble of loving and being loved because we cannot be sure that another human being will *never* let us down. In this way we learn to be fearful of being rejected, especially if we have childhood experiences of it, and this very fear can keep us from being able to love. The fear of loneliness prevents us from making healthy love bonds and ironically makes us more lonely. As babies then, we learn to experience our own personal space and as we grow to become adults we realize that we can function happily in that space, simply by being ourselves.

Putting trust in somebody means that we become vulnerable and this feels dangerous to many people. It is only dangerous in reality if by being vulnerable you are then subject to abuse or misuse, whether physically or emotionally. And this is many people's experience, usually right back in infancy or early childhood. They trusted their parent, usually the mother, and she let them down for some reason, perhaps quite beyond her control. Whatever the original reason, such people can grow up to believe instinctively that however much someone says that they love them, they could still be disappointed.

Having the ability to be truly vulnerable with our partner is central to the concept of intimacy. It involves creating a deep mutual trust, so that any old hurts and harmful lessons from babyhood can be unlearned. This takes time, love and effort and can often prove to be a barrier to true intimacy. Much of the establishment of such trust is carried out at an unconscious level, thus making it difficult or even impossible to deal with rationally, unless you get professional help. Many of the couples that I see have problems, with trust and intimacy at the heart of their troubles, yet no one has ever expressed it to them in this way. Once the subject is raised and steps taken to mend things with love, it is amazing what transformations can occur.

To most people, the word intimacy has to do with sexual or physical closeness, but there is much more to it than that. It can, and often does, involve these things, but this is to view intimacy in a narrow way and can produce real practical problems in everyday life. Intimacy is not just a piece of psychological theory. If I am intimate with my partner it means that I am able to be truly myself in the same space as her, while she is being truly herself. This 'being in touch with someone else in my space' enables me to be in touch with myself. In other words, the most profound experiences of being ourselves occur when we share a space with someone else in this unconditional way.

This definition of intimacy does not mean that I have to be physically close with my partner all the time; on the contrary, such closeness can be the enemy of true intimacy. By being *close* many couples never allow their partner to be themselves – they are always functioning as a part of a two-person system that stifles intimacy. They are too closely enmeshed.

Learning how to be intimate then, is about learning how to enable our partner to be him or herself and to have personal space in which to find themselves. This entails the paradoxical situation of having to be apart from one another to be truly intimate. The couple that can tolerate apartness which provides their partner with his or her own personal space are the better able to be truly intimate. True love is about letting go and not tying our partner down, however unconsciously, so that we can *own* them in some way.

Much of this will sound rather unlikely at first, if the concepts are new to you, but if you try it out in practice you will find that it works. Encourage your partner to do things on his or her own; take an interest but don't take over. Encourage them to develop a personal space and accept the fact that they are uniquely themselves, not merely an extension of you or half of 'a couple'. The liberation that this brings can be amazing.

Of course, all this apartness has to be tempered with a corresponding amount of togetherness, and there are few better ways that I know of a couple finding togetherness and learning about being intimate than on a sensual holiday. This can be any length of time from an evening to a week, in which the two of you make time to be together, to re-discover one another away from the realities of daily life. You can make your 'holiday' at home for an evening with a special meal or you could go to a hotel for a weekend. Carefully prepare for the occasion and take it in turns to make the arrangements so that each of you has a chance to take the lead in what happens. The secret is to return to courtship behaviour and to take real pleasure in trying new things, both in and out of bed. Generate enthusiasm for a weekend holiday by sending one another tokens that can be redeemed on the day. Some good examples are, breakfast in bed, a massage at a time of your choice, a sexual pursuit of your choice, a fantasy to be acted out according to your directions, or a favourite pastime, such as going to a film or gallery. The lead up to the holiday can be every bit as exciting as the event itself.

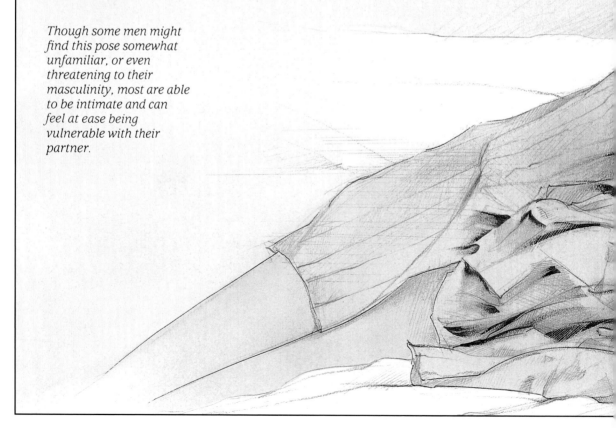

Though some men might find this pose somewhat unfamiliar, or even threatening to their masculinity, most are able to be intimate and can feel at ease being vulnerable with their partner.

You might want to make a no-sex agreement for the first day. Trying to honour it can be fun but many people give up by lunchtime! Whatever you do though, use the time to talk and share, to *be* together rather than having to *do*. Just go for a long walk, sit in a field, or lie on the bed and say nothing. Hold one another and simply communicate soul to soul just by *being*. Much of the time you'll be *doing* and talking too, but be sure not to overwhelm yourselves with too many activities. Your sensual holiday need not just be sex and romance centred. Going round a picture gallery; going shopping together for something special; spending the day sailing or climbing; or doing something that you otherwise would never get around to are all equally valuable. These sorts of activity ensure that you do not spend too much time agonizing about the relationship or getting deeply involved in 'meaningful discussions'. This can be detrimental to the intimacy that should be developing between you. Obviously it is a matter of achieving the right balance but what I am trying to encourage is a blend of doing and being; and of introspection and having fun. If you get this right your holiday will have been far more than just a change and a rest.

When you get home, discuss together what worked and what didn't and immediately plan another holiday so that you can both look forward to it. It need not cost much money but the results are fabulous. Not only is it restful in a busy world but it gives a couple an opportunity to share themselves and simply be together in a way that is either difficult or impossible otherwise. This is a real investment in your relationship.

It is often said that men find it more difficult to be intimate than women but this is not my experience professionally. It is true that many men find it hard to *start* being intimate but this is because we bring up boys to think of such matters as effeminate or sissy. A 'real man' is macho and has immediate intercourse, according to our culture – he doesn't sit around *being* with his partner. Of course, this is a travesty of the truth because men are very concerned with romance, intimacy and love. I find in clinical practice that as soon as I 'give permission' for these subjects to be raised, most men are just as at ease as most women. It is true that most men find it difficult to be open about intimacy as quickly as many women but this is simply a matter of doing something that is unfamiliar, rather than a congenital disability.

A man who feels unconditionally loved and cared for by his partner usually has little difficulty in opening up and being himself within the relationship. The myth that women have a monopoly on feelings has done much to damage one-to-one relationships and discourages many men from even trying, much to their partner's loss. It is certainly very easy to *dis*able a man in this area and it takes some effort at first to *en*able him but it is an investment well worth making. With encouragement most men soon become very able.

What makes sex and marriage so fascinating for me to work with is that true intercourse can be, in my view, the ultimate experience in communication and intimacy between a couple. Indeed, in a largely godless world it could be the nearest that many people get to a spiritual experience. Unfortunately, most couples spend their lives copulating, merely mating rather than having true intercourse, and so miss out on real sexual intimacy, let alone spirituality. Although it might seem confusing to talk of copulation and intercourse as though they were light years apart, my experience tells me that they are in fact very different, especially when one considers intimacy in any realistic way.

The journey from copulation to intercourse starts out of bed with better communication generally. A couple who cannot share their real selves will always copulate rather than have intercourse which is, after all a highly personalized activity tailor-made to the personality of the individuals involved. Commitment is essential; it involves not only the genitals but also the whole personality of the partner; it is part of a couple's whole life style rather than an isolated 'event'; the partner's needs are central; it calls for insight and imagination; it improves with time; it increases the value of the partner; the horizons are limitless; it adapts well to occasional failure; it is based on self-revelation and intimacy; it is based on an uninhibited awareness of possibilities, and is a lifetime investment.

Copulation is *none* of these things, yet can be enjoyable from time to time within a loving and intimate relationship. The notion of 'perfect intercourse' is a harmful myth and even very experienced couples who are able to be truly intimate probably only have 'magic sex' three or four times out of ten. Viewed in this way, copulation is always available and intercourse commonplace within a truly intimate relationship. Even when such a couple are not having sex, however, they are still functioning at a level of intimacy that is rewarding and unique to them. This takes the pressure off genital activities and some such couples can go for long periods without anything genital happening that most would call 'intimate'.

Intimacy then, is something that every couple could benefit from cultivating. It involves levels of selflessness, of other-centred loving, and of spiritual communion that are not likely to be universally attainable. Many couples with whom I deal, however, are surprised at just what is possible once their horizons are broadened and expectations increased.

But most of us find it difficult suddenly to develop intimacy. It requires practice and opportunity, like so much in the romantic and sexual life. Unless we create opportunities in which it can occur, intimacy will never develop. Modern life often makes true intimacy difficult, if only because to learn to be intimate you need to spend a lot of time together and to communicate well about things that matter. The couple whose lives are filled to capacity with other worldly pressures have little or no energy and time to devote to being intimate. Indeed, it is my experience that many such couples quite unconsciously develop this kind of life style so as to avoid true intimacy. Such couples are often doing things *alongside* one another, either as a couple or with their family and friends, yet they are never truly intimate. At the other end of the scale are those couples who *are* very intimate and manage to maintain this sense of intimacy without actually sharing one another's company very much.

As I have pointed out, intimacy demands a substantial amount of togetherness and sharing while you are developing it, yet much of the really important sharing goes on at an unconscious-to-unconscious level in a couple who are attuned to one another and starting to be really intimate. Often there is more intimacy in the silence of sharing a beautiful scene or special event than there is in hours spent talking about it, yet to begin with most couples find that they need to talk things through if they are to communicate their feelings from heart to heart. Later this becomes more intuitive and words become almost redundant on many occasions.

The development of intimacy goes through certain stages – the number and complexity of which vary greatly from couple to couple according to their backgrounds and their ability to be intimate. For some couples their one-to-one bond of commitment to each other is the very first opportunity in their lives for such intimacy to occur. For them things tend to go slowly as they learn to trust each other. For others, from different types of backgrounds, intimacy is already a part of their personality and things progress quickly. Of course, we can marry someone who has a very different model of intimacy from our own and be vexed by it for a whole lifetime, unless we seek help from an outside source.

I hope that, as with many other chapters of this book, the reader might sit down with his or her partner and talk all this through to see what each thinks they mean by intimacy and what, as a result of reading this chapter, they could do to enrich their lives in this area. I find that intimacy is a very difficult subject for most couples to discuss – far, far more demanding than anything to do with sex. It is one thing to be told that you are not the best sex partner in the world but much harder to deal with the fact that your partner does not find he or she can be intimate with you. Of course, this may say a lot more about your partner than you, so be very careful when interpreting what you hear.

Intimacy cannot be manufactured in a relationship but I hope that after working through this chapter with your partner you will be better equipped to think about the subject in a new light.

This couple are being physically intimate but can they also share their souls? Being at ease with one's body is only a part of true vulnerability – it also involves a feeling of emotional safety and trust with one's partner.

LOVE, SEX AND ROMANCE

The words love, sex and romance can all be defined in many different ways, and indeed have been. It is a shame that for many people they all mean the same thing and are interchangeable terms. That this means missing out on a great deal is the subject of this chapter.

Perhaps one of the most difficult tasks confronting new lovers is that of bringing together their needs for and feelings of, love, sex, and romance. We all need to be loved and to love and we learn how to do these things in our childhood. The love we receive from our parents, and others, makes us feel wanted, valued, and worthwhile, and teaches us to be at ease with our bodies. Physical affection is just a part of this, but it is a very important part. Time and again as a therapist I find myself working with individuals for whom all of this is something of a foreign language. They have never really felt loved, cannot truly love anyone, and do not like to touch or be touched.

Defining love is almost impossible but if we judge from what people *do* with regard to the things they love it is clear that they care for them, perhaps jealously guard them, and are concerned for their well-being. Two out of three of these points are other-centred but the jealousy component is very much self-centred. This is probably no bad thing given that we instinctively want to protect things that are valuable to us and so ensure that they do not fall prey to others.

Being 'in love' is quite another matter. This is an almost entirely self-centred emotion in which the loved person is idealized, placed on a pedestal, and judged to be the only one for us. Our love will last for ever. It is like a sickness so disabled are we by it. No one should choose a partner or indeed do anything much else when in this state of unbalanced mind! Once the realities of life dawn though, the idealized partner slowly becomes accepted as a real human being and can be seen as such. During the early stages of being 'in love' our partner is what *we* define them to be; what *we* need them to be; not necessarily what or who they actually are.

As we start to lose this idealized form of love we free ourselves to see the other person as a unique human being rather than a reflection of ourselves and our unconscious needs. Now true love becomes possible. How well we negotiate this particular emotional journey depends almost entirely on how we were brought up; what kind of relationship our parents had; our culturally learned views of love; and much more. Some people never cope with the transition from being 'in love' to real loving and find that as soon as they see themselves as out of love they leave their partner, to find 'true love' with someone else. This often has much to do with an inability to be truly intimate, a subject we looked at on page 30.

As love grows within a good relationship both partners enable one another to grow; to find themselves; to change; and to make the most of their personalities. This facilitating role of lovers is, in my view, one of the signs of *real* love in its broadest and most spiritual sense.

Sex fits into all of this because it is one way that we have of demonstrating our love. Being physically intimate with someone takes us back to our first love bond in the cradle when our mother cared for us, cherished us, answered our needs, made us feel trusting and safe, and had our best interests at heart. All of this can be recreated by those who make love, by my definition of the phrase (see page 34). Indeed, intercourse is mainly about regression to childhood and its pleasures. There are precious few times in adult life when we can be wholly ourselves, totally trusting and open, feeling loved, loving, touching, being touched, and giving and receiving delicious erotic sensations. To be able to do all this at one and the same time, as one can in intercourse, is a very powerful pleasure indeed. If in addition to all these bodily sensations, we can also feel a deeper sense of spiritual contentedness, then we build a bond that transcends almost anything else we are likely to experience as humans.

Within this context, sex is a sort of emotional, physical, psychological and spiritual glue that binds a couple together. In my experience as a marital therapist good sex *can* keep couples together even if their lives are otherwise highly disrupted by events outside their relationship. It is amazing how powerful the combination of love and sex can be – it appears to be able to overcome almost any adversity.

Compared with this kind of bond and its rewards, the joys of promiscuity or even the odd affair, pale into insignificance. Such encounters may have a temporary attraction, but within the one-to-one relationship the loss can be great – even possibly for ever. Once trust has been lost it requires a lot of rebuilding, even in quite trusting people, but if knowledge of the affair has been coupled with catching a venereal disease, perhaps with adverse effects on the 'innocent' partner, the relationship can be seriously threatened.

Romance is a subject that few therapists seem to make much of and I find this easy to understand because the subject is so difficult. It is far easier to get people to talk openly about their sex lives than it is about their concepts of romance. Yet romantic fiction is a vast area of publishing and is growing in popularity among women of all ages and social groups. Clearly there is a real need among women for romance – a need, they often tell me, that is unfulfilled in their everyday lives. Most men are, to all intents and purposes, inarticulate on the subject of romance but it is possible, after a while, to encourage them to open up and be just as enthusiastic about it as are women.

Romantic love emerges strongly in late adolescence as the mid-adolescent stage of being in love with oneself matures. The young person now tries to find an ideal partner in whom to invest all this excess love. When a loved one is chosen, feelings of love and notions about sex come together for the first time.

Here romantic love still has more to do with the self than with the loved person. There is almost a preoccupation with our own feelings, which might at first appear strange because romance appears to be centred on the other person. Those in this phase of romantic love write poems about it, sing songs about it, and write letters to their beloved. Both in fiction and in fact, such romantic love is beset with anxiety, yearning, and even depression. This is what people mean when they talk of the 'agony of being in love'. In a sense pain is a real part of romantic love. Some women never grow out of this stage and remain tragedy queens all their lives. They often have very good relationships but spoil them, quite unconsciously of course, by creating traumas that they feel are necessary to complete their concept of romantic love. There has to be pain and suffering.

But this phase of adolescence does not last for ever in most of us; we learn from it and become less self-centred and more realistic. 'Calf' love or 'puppy' love is often made fun of by parents and other adults but we all have to learn, and to shame youngsters as some do, is to harm them unnecessarily at a time when they are especially vulnerable.

However, romance is not all immature or 'bad'. On the contrary, it is a valued part of adult, loving and caring relationships, that most of us ignore at our peril. The difference is that in a mature relationship romance is *added in* little by little rather than being at the very heart of the matter. In this way, we accept our partner for their real selves *and* have the advantages of romance. It is almost impossible to reverse this script successfully.

According to most studies, the romantic portion of marriage diminishes with time. Some people, and especially women, say that this means that love itself has gone from the relationship. This need not necessarily be so. Such a woman would then look for a new partner, usually after 'de-loving' her existing one; or go straight for a divorce. Men who become disillusioned with the loss of romance either go for affairs of the 'my-wife-doesn't-understand-me' type, or invest increasing amounts of time pursuing hobbies or their job. Then what usually happens is that the couple start to punish one another, perhaps using sex as the weapon, and soon even that love which they had, dies.

Romance need not necessarily die with the passing of the years. Keeping it alive can be fun and rewarding and continuing to court each other is one sure way of achieving this. However, by far the best way is through exciting and fulfilling lovemaking. When we have good sex we regress to both babyhood and the late teens and re-awaken adolescent romantic ideals. Having re-immersed ourselves in those magical feelings of love, commitment, and esteem for our partner, the effects spill over into life together out of bed. Regular top-ups of romance during lovemaking can be all that many couples need, but others find that they enjoy enriching their romantic lives; giving and receiving presents 'for no reason'; being exceptionally attentive and kind to their partner; taking every opportunity to show their love for one another in non-genital ways; kissing and cuddling more; sharing interests and hobbies together; phoning for no reason except to say 'I love you'; leaving little love notes around the house where they will be found; going out together as if they were on an early date; thinking about how they could improve their appearance; or taking time to enjoy a sensual holiday together. Holidays can be a wonderful source of romance. We look at these more on page 32.

Skin-to-skin contact within a close relationship often says more about love, sex and romance than can any number of words.

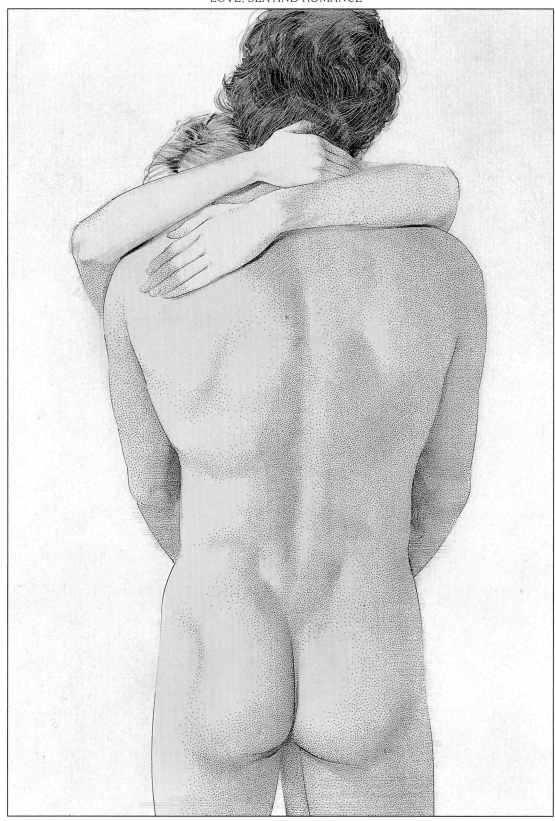

Many women complain of a lack of warmth in their relationship and many men that the girl they loved so intensely and romantically has gone, but this is often brought about because of differing definitions of what really *is* romantic. The suggestions outlined above are generally considered to be romantic by men and women but once we stray outside this somewhat restricted list, romance becomes less well defined. To men, romance seems to include a continuing, faithful, dedicated, trouble-free, reliable, sexually fulfilling and exclusive relationship. To women, the romantic connotations of their relationship are more often linked to settings and events. A woman often refers to a particular meal, hotel, piece of music, or a memorable lovemaking session, when she talks of romance. Communicating with each other about romance can be a problem as most people encounter embarrassment about the subject, after their adolescence – which is where they probably learned to be embarrassed about it in the first place. Some people say that if they have to tell their partner how to be romantic, any appeal is lost. Their partner is somehow supposed to 'know'. Loving discussion can usually overcome these problems and a sensitive couple generally find a path that suits them both.

It makes sense then to be careful not to assume that your partner's ideas of romance are the same as yours. Pay attention to what he or she wants and needs if your life together is to be romantic by their definition. Slowly, and perhaps with some effort, you'll be able to blend your ideas of romance so that you are both delighted much of the time, if by different things. Remember that difference can be every bit as delicious as similarity in romance.

Problems with definitions plague all of our loving lives together because not only do we have different views about what constitutes romance but also what love and, indeed sex, really are. 'A man who really loved me would/wouldn't do that' is the sort of thing I mean. I often have to spend quite some time encouraging couples to define what they think they mean by all these highly emotive words.

Even 'sex' is open to a myriad of conflicting definitions within one relationship. To some it means intercourse, to others all sorts of sexual activities, and to yet others it is another word for love. A large number of people of both sexes, but particularly women, believe that sex must be accompanied by love. If it is not and they want sex, they unconsciously drum up some 'love' and declare it, so that they can excuse their genital needs. The confusion here is especially apparent to me when I am dealing with those who are having an affair. It is my view that most women seek affairs believing that they are looking for love and find sex, and that most men having affairs believe they are looking for sex and find love. Whichever way round it is, we could all benefit enormously by looking more honestly at how we think of these areas of our lives and try to separate them out one from another.

Sorting out such complex matters can be difficult. A technique I find useful is to ask couples to sit down at home and write down their definitions of each of the words. They are then asked to write what they think their partner's definition of each of the words is. Next, they take each one in turn and say how they would like things in their lives to change so that they could have each area made perfect, or more nearly so.

Having done this, I suggest that they exchange their notes and read what one another has written. This then opens the subject up to discussion. Of course, this exploration can occur more openly and less dangerously in a therapeutic setting but with care a couple should be able to tackle the same task at home.

The main danger when discussing such personal areas is that you find yourselves expressing hurt, or worse, when you begin to realize just how different your partner's views are. The secret of success is to listen as much as you talk and to remember that what your partner says might not be his or her last words on the subject. Indeed, it might be their *first* thoughts, perhaps hesitantly and inexpertly expressed. After all, few people ever undertake this task together in their lives. This working through of ideas should be carried out tenderly and lovingly as each of you feels your own way and seeks to find the common ground between you.

After completing such a discussion write down a list of the things that you have managed to agree upon. This ends the session positively and helps you see just how much you *do* have in common, however much you also find you disagree on. Arrange another get-together fairly soon, to recommence where you left off so that you can develop the topics that you will by then have had more time to think about.

There are no school courses, few books, and almost no after-marriage courses that look at these difficult matters, so most couples who want to explore such ideas usually find themselves not doing it at all or slowly making their own discoveries as the years go by.

It can often be helpful to discuss the subjects of love, sex and romance with a really close friend, if you have one. By bouncing ideas off someone else we can often come to see our partner's point of view in a more balanced light and return to our next talk with fresh insights or at least from a more understanding and positive stance.

Because the words love, sex and romance are so heavily weighted and so hard to define it is not surprising that many couples have great difficulty talking about them at all. Yet, I find that even quite a small amount of time devoted to discussion can clear the air in a relationship and resolve all kinds of long-standing misunderstandings.

Many couples have problems relating to one or more of these areas of their life together yet they are often matters of definition or perception rather than true differences that mean they have to continue with problems or even break up. They are, after all, some of the most highly charged words in our language as lovers and, as a result, are open to considerable differences of interpretation.

By confusing love, sex and romance we run the risk of missing out on the joys and unique pleasures of each. Sex is not romance; romance is not love; and love is not sex. Each has its own delights; its own history in our lives; each its own future for us; each its own significance to our partner. Only by talking about all of this with our beloved is it possible to begin to see where we are in the shared double triangle of love, sex and romance. The secret of success is to find where our triangles intersect and to build from the common points we share. It is then a matter of constant growth and exploration to make things better and better as the years go by.

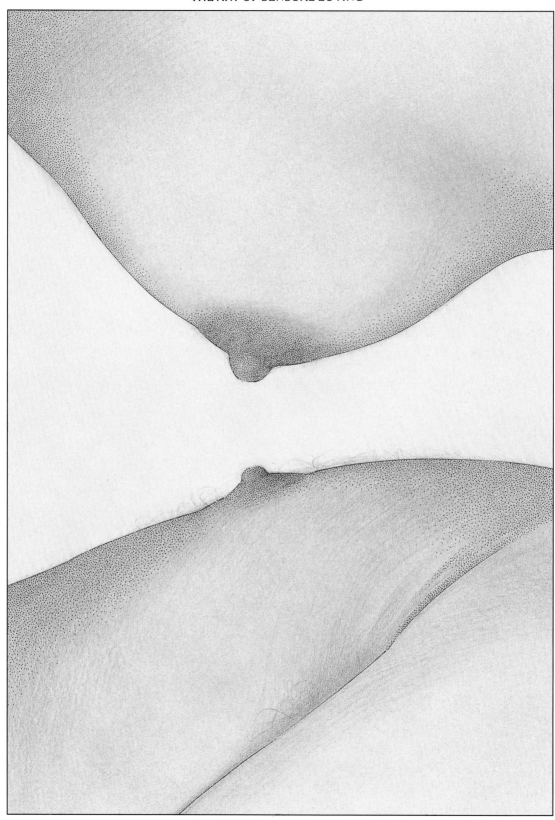

CHAPTER THREE

ENHANCING YOUR SEXUAL BODY

Sex is a complex activity involving mind, body and spirit.
In this chapter we look at the body as the temple of our
sexuality. Whilst it is often difficult to understand or even
perceive what is happening to our minds when we are
engaged in sexual activities, it is much easier to be aware
of our bodies. Even so, many people are not well
informed about their bodies. This chapter tries
to put this right.

SEX FROM HEAD TO TOE

*Our bodies reveal much about our sexuality and most people
claim that it is a person's body that they first notice when
assessing them as a potential partner. The way we use, abuse,
adorn, hold, shape, and deal with our bodies is vitally
important, not only in attracting a new partner but in keeping
our existing one.*

Few people I deal with have a neutral view of their body, even though when I first raise the subject they may claim otherwise. The truth is that we all know what we feel about our bodies, even if we rarely discuss our feelings. I find that it is useful and therapeutic to go through each part of the body in some detail, encouraging the individual to share what they like and do not like about their bodies. It is surprising how much valuable material is gained from such a session, information that gives me various clues to the individual's life style, fears, pleasures and pains, and most importantly, their sexuality.

This is an exercise that lovers can employ too, with some care. If you really love one another and are not trying to score points, then it can be enlightening to learn what you each think about your own physical appearance. Save sharing what you think about each other's bodies until you are really sure of one another and can be safely personal knowing that there will be no cruel, hurtful criticism involved.

Start, as I do, by considering a fairly safe area such as the feet and legs. Work your way through the anatomy area by area, until you come to the more sensitive emotional regions such as a woman's breasts and a man's penis. If you find that you can easily dispel a fear or concern your partner might have, then do so at once. For example, a woman might say, 'I wish I had blonde hair but otherwise it's quite nice'. Her partner could then reply, 'I love you as you are. I wouldn't fancy you with blonde hair. I love brunettes'. Or, if he really would like her to experiment with going blonde for a while he could encourage her to do so and then be sympathetic if it were not a successful change.

Our views of our own bodies are coloured by all kinds of fears experienced during childhood and adolescence. These fears may no longer be true *in fact* but they linger on in our unconscious and have a tendency to hurt when we least want them to. A loving partner can help redress this because he or she loves us the way we are. It is fascinating when talking to women about their body shape, style, blemishes, and bulges, to realise just how critical they are. This has undoubtedly occurred because in our society the body beautiful reigns supreme and women have, rather wickedly, been brainwashed into thinking that they have to have perfect bodies to be acceptable. The interesting thing is that most men when confronted with such downbeat comments from their partners in therapy, say things such as, 'What varicose veins?', 'What stretch marks?', 'I don't know what she means by being fat, I think she's great as she is', 'To be honest, I'd forgotten about her appendix scar', and so on.

Of course, not everyone thinks like this and many have grounds for some complaint about how their partner looks. For many couples, this is just one of the 'no go' areas in their relationship and one that calls for prudent management. Her tiny breasts, his beer belly, or whatever, need to be discussed with extreme sensitivity if hackles are not to rise. Having said this, it is a lazy and arrogant lover who does not take into account what their partner reveals during a discussion of such issues. Just because we are living with or married to someone, we do not have a license to neglect our appearance and disregard the consequences. Unfortunately, I see far too many couples for whom this is a way of life. They then wonder why it is that the other is unconsciously punishing them in some way, in or out of bed.

Our personal body style dictates not only how we think of ourselves but also how we are perceived by the world. For example, according to research, a tall man is almost always seen as being more forceful and attractive than a short one. Physically attractive people of both sexes are presumed by others to be more successful, and more sexually active. In other words, how we look makes people suppose certain things about us, even if they are not correct. These erroneous assumptions can play havoc in our lives. Perhaps the best example of this is revealed by a household name patient of mine who receives scores of marriage proposals every week, so gorgeous is she. Yet in her real life she is shy, unable to deal with men and lives a quiet, almost lonely life. Her fans would not recognize her in her private life.

The appearance we create comes from a perfectly conscious effort made to achieve an image that we think is attractive. But it also emanates from quite unconscious mechanisms of which we are, by definition, unaware. We saw on page 22 how revealing body language is and that the vast majority of this is not under conscious control. Yet it reveals so much about us. Experiments with specially designed eye cameras that enable researchers to monitor exactly what people are looking at at any given moment, show that people look at rather different things than they claim when assessing a person of the opposite sex. Most of us have made a decision within a few seconds as to whether someone is likely to be a suitable partner. We do this whether or not we are consciously seeking a partner. First impressions are clinched by the initial messages we receive about a person's body shape, style, clothes, posture, size, and their personality as demonstrated by these characteristics. All this is summarized in a few seconds and we then act accordingly.

Once past the looking stage, how a person uses their body to sexually attract or repel another person also has a profound effect. For instance, very tactile people can be arousing for some personality types and extremely irritating for others. By and large the British are a 'no-touch' culture whereas many European, and especially Mediterranean peoples, are highly tactile both heterosexually and homosexually. How much we touch and like to be touched greatly depends on childhood experiences and our current loving and sexual life. But make no mistake, early messages about sexual availability, or otherwise, are powerfully transmitted by touch even at a social level.

It is not socially acceptable to touch one another intimately but as a couple explore their sexualities during courtship and become more at ease with one

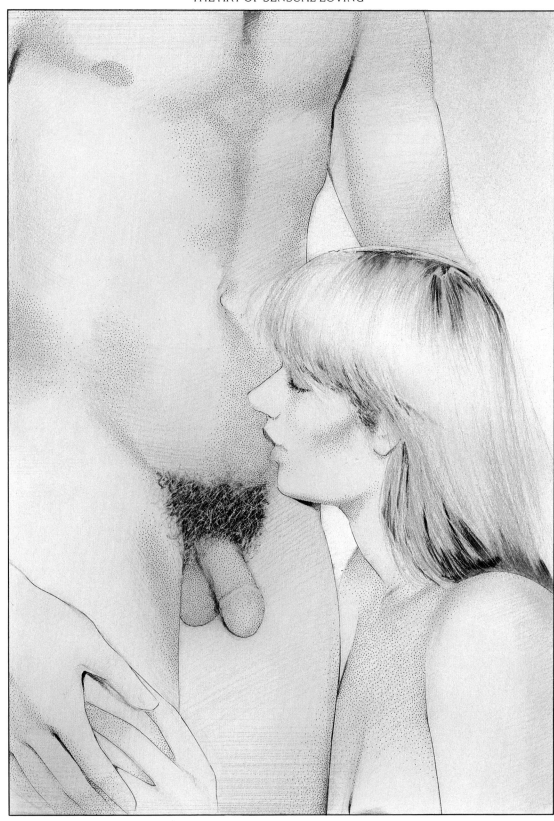

another's bodies, it soon becomes apparent that there are areas of the body that have greater sexual significance in terms of arousal. These are called the erogenous zones. As I point out through this book, almost any area of the body can be sexually exciting if the right stimulus is created by the right person, but erogenous zones are rather different. These areas produce sexual arousel even if the individual stimulating them is not a loved partner.

In general, there are more highly sexually arousable areas on a woman's body. Women can be brought to orgasm by all kinds of non-genital pursuits, that men could not possibly be affected by. We will see in the following section on skin and lovemaking that different areas of the body respond in varying ways to touch and sensations created by other means, but the erogenous zones are fairly predictable in their response. The most receptive areas are the genitals, and in women especially the clitoris, the vulva and the lower third of the vagina. A woman's breasts and nipples can be highly erotic too, but this is not true for all women. The anal area in both sexes is far more arousing than many realize, as is the perineum, in between the genitals and the anus.

Apart from his nipples, a man is really only *highly* erogenous in the area including his groin, genitals, buttocks and anus, but of course, as arousal proceeds, many other areas of his body become more valuable in this respect. What produces the most arousing sensations in any one erogenous zone will be for you to discover as a couple but as I point out in the next section it helps to be adventurous, experimenting beyond simply stroking, kissing and cuddling.

But lovemaking starts well before we get to the stage of caressing one another's erogenous zones. The way we dress and decorate ourselves suggests to our partner features of our bodies that we consider attractive. So it is that a woman who is at ease with her breasts might wear a pendant that takes a man's eyes down to her cleavage and a good bra that displays her breasts to best advantage. She could be suggesting that she enjoys having her breasts caressed during lovemaking. Similarly, a man could wear tight jeans and stand with his thumbs hooked into his belt with his fingers pointing down to his genitals when chatting up such a woman at a party. This may be an extreme example, but they are both, usually quite unconsciously, pointing out the parts of their bodies that they will want stimulated should things go further. All this is part of the game of courtship and attraction that is an instinctive part of human behaviour whether or not we are on the look-out for a mate. Problems can arise however, when our body language says one thing and our mind unconsciously means another. Conflicting messages such as this are at the heart of much social misunderstanding and subsequent affairs.

A helpful exercise that you can do as a couple is to take a piece of paper each and then draw how you see first yourself and then your partner. Do not go for artistic excellence – in fact you could even draw in a highly symbolic way. Some people asked to do this create vegetable images for their partner.

Although his main erogenous zone is the area including his genitals and groin, she is teasing him by kissing the area around it, increasing the thrill of his anticipation.

When you have both done this in private, exchange pictures and talk about what you have created. This exercise often enables a couple to be far more open about concerns that they have about both their own and their partner's body style. Of course, as with any of the games that I suggest throughout the book, this one only works well if both partners are honest and treat each other with sensitivity and respect.

Our bodies are truly our shop windows. They can display what we consciously want to say about ourselves but often they do far more than this. Being aware of what our bodies say both in and out of bed, is a part of being a responsible and responsive lover.

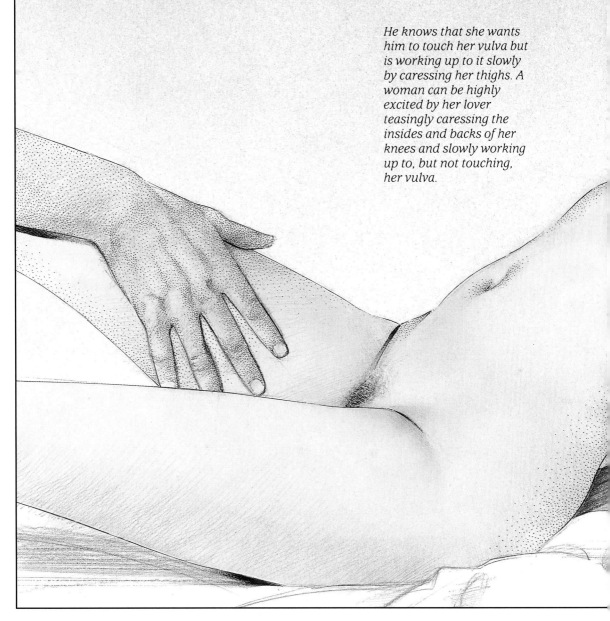

He knows that she wants him to touch her vulva but is working up to it slowly by caressing her thighs. A woman can be highly excited by her lover teasingly caressing the insides and backs of her knees and slowly working up to, but not touching, her vulva.

TOUCHING AND BEING TOUCHED

The skin is the largest organ of the body and because it collects more information about sexual activity than any other organ it is of special interest to us here. The way we use our skin in lovemaking can make all the difference between an ordinary experience and a magical one.

The skin of an average adult weighs four kilograms (9 lb) and covers more than two square metres (21½ sq ft). The myriad of sensations that it can perceive, of many at a time, gives us a tremendous sensuous potential to make sex much more than just enjoyable.

Because the skin can tell us about temperature, fine touch, pressure, pain, vibration and much more besides, it gives us almost constant feedback as to the aroused state of our body as we make love. The art of touching is central to good sex and we all have a unique pattern of sensations that we find affects us best. This might be to arouse or to soothe us, depending on the situation.

The sensory part of the brain is divided into areas that receive inputs from all the different parts of the body. Some areas are much more richly represented than others because of the number of sensory inputs that are received from that part of the body. For example, the hands, lips, face and feet are best represented. Surprisingly, the genitals are not as sensitive as the toes when it comes to touch, but that is not to say that they are insensitive generally. Any experienced lover will know that the shaft of a man's penis is not all that sensitive to touch, nor is a woman's vagina along much of its length.

Knowledge of these facts should help lovers who want to achieve the best possible pleasure together. It is no accident that petting involves the head and neck because not only are these areas easily accessible but the largest sensory regions of the brain are devoted to them. This is why so many people especially enjoy having their neck, ears, lips, face and tongue kissed.

However, the hands, thumbs and fingers tend to be overlooked and this is a shame. One male patient of mine can nearly have an orgasm when his wife sucks his thumb as they make love. This is not because he used to suck it as a child, he did not, but because the fingers are so highly endowed with sensory receptors. This makes sucking one another's fingers and toes an exquisite pastime yet it is one that is often totally overlooked by lovers.

Bearing all this in mind, it should now be clear that couples that really want to get the best from their sensual life together should go to some lengths to map out each other's sensual areas. When you do this, ensure that you are fairly aroused to start with and then take it in turns, perhaps on different occasions, to try out various types of stimulation on different areas of your partner's body. Try light touch, firm touch, smacking, hot, cold, sharp sensations, and use materials such as fur, silk, leather or rubber. Blowing air across wetted skin can be highly arousing. Rub in some cream that you might otherwise use for sore muscles and see what sort of arousing effect it has.

When experimenting, you might tend to be more cautious than is really necessary so be brave and try out new sensations. As you experiment with something novel get your partner to score it out of five. If something is at all good, try to make it better by enhancing what you do or the way that you do it so that you reach four or five before going on to the next area or type of sensation.

Hard sensations such as smacking, biting or pinching are enjoyed by many lovers, especially when they are aroused. It is vital to remember that sensations change as we become aroused, so that something like a silly slap on a Sunday afternoon in front of TV which was greatly disliked, can become a real favourite if the individual is highly aroused.

Generally we tend to be too cautious as we play with one another sexually. Because 'nice' people just stroke and cuddle, many lovers can tend to miss out the pleasurable skin sensations so easily available. For example, a man might think that her breasts are tender objects that should be kept wrapped in cotton wool. He may have gained this impression because by touching them too early in her arousal cycle she complained or because her breasts are too sensitive before a period to be handled much at all. But, at other times of the month, such women often tell me they wish their partner would do more to their breasts and do so with some ardour. We tend to think of nipples as so sensitive that they should be handled with silk gloves but many people of both sexes enjoy their nipples being squeezed, even quite hard, as they near orgasm. Some women are keen to experience what could be considered pain at this time, yet are too shy to ask in case it is thought to be perverted.

Smacking can be deliciously erotic. Blood flow to the skin is increased and in the buttock area this might increase blood flow to the genitals. Since sexual arousal is mainly linked to increased blood flow to an area of the body, it is hardly surprising that the brain registers one and links it to the other. This is why so many couples find smacking one another's bottoms so arousing. If one or the other is unconsciously inhibited about sex, as is often the case, then it is not difficult to see that some sort of 'punishment', however symbolic, also helps to defuse the guilt the person feels for wanting sex at all. These, and other mechanisms, are at the heart of many so-called sado-masochistic games that couples play. The inflicting of pain as a part of sexual arousal is not a modern concept and can be explained on many levels. At the simplest, it is a sign that you fancy one another furiously and want to take or be taken roughly. At the other end of the scale, it could be that one or other of you has unusual needs in some deeper psychological way, that could perhaps benefit from professional help. The vast majority of couples who indulge in such games though are neither weird nor perverted, they have simply found that the skin's response to pain crosses with its response to pleasure. Perhaps the raised level of stress hormones caused by the 'pain' also stimulates the body in ways that it recognizes as sexual because during stress and sex similar hormones are mobilized by the body.

Given that the skin is so important in lovemaking, it makes sense to look after it. Be especially careful about the skin of your hands as they most frequently come into contact with your partner's body. Try to keep this skin clean, free from nicotine stains, with short nails, and soft, sensitive fingertips. If your hands are clumsy from doing hard physical work you may find that doing something detailed such as model-making or sewing will help your hands become more sensitive and flexible in massage and lovemaking. Apart from washing regularly, the rest of the body's skin does not need any special attention. Our culture tends to emphasize hair removal, especially for women, who often see themselves as unsexy if they are more hairy in certain places. If you and your partner can agree about what is sexy for you then try not to be too influenced by what others say. Some men, for example, like their partner to keep her under-arm hair and some men like hairy legs. Other men find that almost total depilation is to their taste, except on the head, of course. Find a middle way that you can both live with and you could perhaps make your body hair care a part of your sexual life together. Many couples cut one another's hair, or nails, as part of mutual grooming and some women are sexually aroused by their men shaving a part of them, perhaps their bikini line and genital area, as a prelude to intercourse.

Caring for one another's skin can also become a part of your daily lovemaking. Washing one another's backs, massaging oil or lotion into the skin, or even just caressing each other naked can all help to maintain the value and function of this vital sex organ.

This woman is concentrating on his skin. Her hair is caressing him, as is much of her body, and she is adding to the deliciousness of it all by blowing gently into his navel. Although this gentle breath does not actually involve any direct skin contact, it is probably the most arousing of all.

UNDERSTANDING AROUSAL

*A thorough knowledge of our partner's sexual arousal is vital if
we are to be able to interpret accurately their reactions in
sexual situations. Far too many couples never learn how to read
one another properly and spend their sexual life together
working from misunderstandings. This problem can be easily
overcome and in this section we see how.*

Sexual arousal is a highly complex affair involving our mind, body, spirit, and
all our senses. The magic of what makes one person 'click' with another is
not understood by modern science but we are beginning to obtain clues from a
knowledge of substances such as pheromones – consciously imperceptible
smells that act as sexual attractants in most animals.

Physical sexual attraction is but one factor in what arouses us about our
partner and the couple who know one another intimately can become aroused
by even the tiniest of sexual messages, such as the smell of one another's sweat
or genital fluids; the sight of a particular part of the body; hearing their voice on
the phone; a secret piece of love-talk; feeling a familiar garment or a part of
their body; and so on. It is as though we weave a complex tapestry of arousal
messages within a relationship and that one small thread of that tapestry can
trigger off the whole picture in our minds.

Some people can become aroused just by *thinking* about their beloved. A few
women have told me that they have orgasms thinking about their partner – in
the absence of any other stimulation. Most of us need some sort of physical
stimulation if we are to become fully aroused, that is, enough to have
intercourse. It is the physical response that we shall spend more time
considering, because it is this that we can readily perceive and deal with.

In both men and women, physical sexual arousal occurs in much the same
way. Basically, it involves a considerable increase in blood flow to the sexual
organs, accompanied by general body changes. Recent research carried out in
the United States has found that sexual arousal is in fact very similar indeed in
the two sexes – far more so than was originally thought by the pioneering sex
researchers of the 1960s.

In the woman, changes that are readily apparent to both herself and her
partner are a swelling of the breasts and the genitals. The first signs of a
woman's sexual arousal are that her nipples erect and swell. The breast skin
may become flushed and the veins more obvious. The flush is a measles-like
rash that can spread from the breasts themselves to the neck, chest, and even
the face.

The next sign is that her vulva swells. The inner lips especially become
engorged with blood and darken in colour. The vagina starts to expand and
'sweats' fluid from its walls to lubricate the vaginal cavity. Some of this fluid
may appear at the vaginal entrance or even flow profusely over the inner and
outer lips to make the whole area wet.

Now the clitoris begins to erect. In some women it can enlarge to twice its normal size but in others the increase in size hardly shows at all. As the woman becomes more aroused, the swelling of the whole vulval area can mask enlargement of the clitoris and it can be difficult to find.

The outer vaginal lips also swell and become darker and the vagina opens up a little at its entrance. Inside the vagina the top starts to open up like a tent and the lower third of the vagina swells more than the rest to produce a warm spongy, soft area of tissue that will eventually grip the penis tightly. At the same time, the rest of a woman's body is also undergoing changes. As her breasts swell, her heart beats faster, she sweats, her breathing increases in speed, and her body starts to twitch. Often the first signs of this high state of arousal are that her toes, feet or tummy muscles start to flutter or twitch.

As she reaches orgasm her body may arch, she may emit a cry, her face may grimace, and her body muscles generally go tense. Her vaginal, uterine, and pelvic muscles all contract strongly and rhythmically and her whole body may be thrown into involuntary spasms. How a woman actually responds as she climaxes depends greatly on her upbringing; her personality type; her previous sexual experiences; her mood on the day; her level of excitement; the current environment; the intensity of the occasion; and how she thinks her sexuality is perceived by her partner.

Once the contractions of her vaginal, uterine and pelvic muscles stop, she is still capable of further stimulation to another orgasm, though many women do not go on to this stage, for various reasons. Some women can experience many orgasms one after the other, and I have patients who have fluttering mini-orgasms repeatedly for many minutes in such a way as to claim that they have a 'ten minute orgasm'. Some women need a lot more stimulation if they are to have more than one orgasm but some men are not prepared to do this, feeling that the woman can caress herself to complete her satisfaction. Other women find that their second and subsequent orgasms are achieved with little extra stimulation.

A knowledge of all of this, gleaned from experience of watching a woman masturbating herself (see page 115) is a worthy investment for any loving relationship. A man who cares for and wants to please his partner will learn how to tell where she is in her arousal cycle by looking, feeling and listening. An experienced lover – experienced with his woman that is, because women vary so greatly in the detail of their arousal patterns – can tell exactly how excited his partner is by feeling how wet she is. A woman's arousal can be judged by her wetness as a man's can be judged by the state of his erection. Breast changes also give very good clues but erect nipples can be caused by cold, fear, or even the slightest touch in some women. A sex flush is a sure sign that she is nearing an orgasm and is one that no woman can fake. Because few women like to be asked if they are nearing their orgasm this can be a valuable sign for a man.

Many misunderstandings arise because a man does not know where his partner is in her arousal cycle. He stimulates her either too much or too little or perhaps inappropriately because he is not sufficiently vigilant in monitoring the changing state of her body. Of course, a woman can help by being more

communicative about how aroused she feels so that her man can learn to link what he observes with what she says she is feeling. Once this has been learned though, a couple will not need to keep discussing it. We see on page 115 how it is possible to become aware of the valuable signs of arousal by watching one another masturbate.

Arousal in a man starts in the mind, just as in a woman. Messages travel from the brain to the penis, which starts to swell as a result of blood damming up within it. It changes from the small, downward-pointing, limp, organ to a hard, upward, rigid, rod-like one. No man can will an erection but high levels of excitement and arousal can take a small, half-hearted erection to a full and useful one within seconds. Many, even quite experienced women, get annoyed when their man will not erect when they want him to but there is no way that he can control it consciously. The trigger mechanisms for erections are very delicate. As someone who sees men with problems, it amazes me that erections occur as easily and apparently effortlessly as they do. In some men the slightest noise, distraction, illness, lack of stimulation, thoughtless remark, or whatever, can kill even a strong, budding erection. This puts men at a basic biological disadvantage because they have to have a hard erection if intercourse is to occur whereas a woman can use something to lubricate herself, if necessary. Of course, she will not experience the same enjoyment as from highly arousing intercourse but in biological terms she can function.

As a man's penis erects, changes are occurring elsewhere, just as in a woman's body. His heartbeat quickens, his breathing speeds up, he sweats more, his pupils get larger, his nostrils flare, his blood pressure rises, his muscles tense, and he feels sexual tension mounting inside him. About one man in four has a sex flush rather like that of a woman, and during this phase of growing excitement his scrotum contracts and his testes move to lie closer to his body. Up to this stage a man can halt his excitement and return to a resting stage even if he feels disappointment at doing so. Within a few minutes he'll feel normal

The touch, smell, taste, feel and sound of their bodies are all arousing sensations as they luxuriate in one another. Any one of these senses can arouse the seasoned lover because he or she is so attuned to what excites them about the other.

again. More usually though he will go on to have an orgasm. In the next phase of his arousal the penis swells more, changes colour to become blue-purple especially at the tip, the testes swell and he is now committed to having an orgasm. There is no turning back. Most men can recognize this stage easily and have some control over the speed of progress from here on. Those that do not have this awareness are prone to premature ejaculation because the warning signs of imminent ejaculation are not apparent to them.

At orgasm the man has to ejaculate – he has no choice. His pelvic muscles contract, as do all the muscles of his genital organs and he spurts semen from the penis. Even before this, a little fluid leaks out of the penis which can contain sperms and so can make a woman pregnant. How many spurts a man has and how far they travel depends on many things, such as his age; how long it is since he last ejaculated; his level of excitement; how he is being stimulated; and so on. The rate of spurting his ejaculate is exactly the same as that of a woman's orgasm contractions – one every eight-tenths of a second.

Eventually, after ejaculation, the man relaxes, his penis regains its usual size and his body goes back to normal. He now has to rest for a while before being able to repeat the cycle. This so-called 'refractory period' varies greatly from man to man and especially with age. Some young men in their twenties can have orgasm after orgasm, like a woman, but as a man ages he needs more time to recover. A man of fifty or sixty years old might not be able to ejaculate again for a day or so.

The hardness of a man's erection is not the best indicator of his level of arousal. Many men can be highly aroused yet have a poor erection. This happens if he is very tired, not ready for sex, or is impotent. Inserting the penis in this half-erect state is not a futile occupation because many men can obtain a really useful and enjoyable erection from this, somewhat poor, start. Far too many women fail to make the best of an erection on the basis that if he really wanted sex or was at all in love with her, he would have a sturdy erection and double-quick! This is, unfortunately, not so. Indeed, I often say to couples that if intercourse were to rely on female sexual arousal being as high as it needs to be in men there would be precious few babies around! Few men can resist their penis being kissed or sucked and whilst it is true that there are occasions when a man might find it difficult to achieve an erection, an orally stimulated penis rarely fails to quickly become firm.

Many women find it difficult to know when their partner is about to ejaculate. Indeed it *can* be difficult to know. Some men have a final increase in penis size just beforehand; some have a particular blissful expression on their face that their partner comes to know well; some have very specific scrotal changes (their testes come to lie tight up against the body); and others push very hard into their partner just before they ejaculate.

Just as many women complain that far too many men go straight for their breasts and nipples too early on in their arousal cycle so too men say that women can think only of their penis. Men greatly enjoy having their nipples played with and other areas of arousal outlined on page 49 are exciting too. When stimulating a man, a woman needs to be especially careful because some judgement of timing is required. If a man is not to reach a climax too soon for his or his partner's liking she will have to spend some time learning to understand and recognize his timing so that she does not overdo things and then find herself complaining that he achieves orgasm too easily. Surprisingly, many men are shy to ask for what they want, either to speed them up or slow them down, but a couple that can share such knowledge with each other will have precious few problems with premature or retarded ejaculation. The woman who knows her man well can time his ejaculation to suit her orgasm. Whilst I never suggest aiming for simultaneous orgasm as a sexual way of life, it certainly helps to be able to have at least some control over a man's apparently uncontrollable orgasms. The couples that master this have something that will stand them in good stead for a whole sexual lifetime together.

In the past, when many more people embarked on their one-to-one relationship from a base of fairly minimal knowledge of the opposite sex they learned about sexual arousal in the context of their lifetime partner. Today though, things are very different. About ninety-four per cent of all couples have had sexual experience to intercourse before marriage and many individuals have had several partners before they settle down. Extramarital sex is also very common in both sexes.

This increased sexual experience brings some advantages but it can also cause confusion. For the couple who have only ever known one another sexually, lessons can be learned and methods of arousal can be tailor-made to suit that individual. But with increasing exposure to other people's sexuality, notions of what might be acceptable or interesting to a new partner colour reality and can often obstruct the path of true mutual discovery.

Most of us tend to learn from experience and then apply this experience to our new partner. In matters to do with sex this is often not all that helpful because people can be so different in the way they achieve arousal. This is especially true of women.

This can often make a 'highly experienced' man something of a nuisance because he makes assumptions about how best to arouse a new partner on the basis of other women he has known and pleasured. His experience makes him feel an expert but he is not an expert on his new partner, however much he might know about other women. He is not taking into account the fact that he is meeting a new woman, a new person altogether.

It should be apparent that a basic humility is required, to be open to learning afresh with a new partner rather than trying to make him or her fit the stereotype that we have created for ourselves as a result of previous experience. The fact that many people create this kind of sexual straitjacket for their partner leads to all kinds of confusion and trouble. It is but a short step from seeing one's partner as different, to thinking that he or she is somehow odd, inhibited or perverted. Needless to say, this kind of assumption, spoken or not, can lead to misunderstanding and resentment.

We have just seen how you can learn to understand your partner's sexual arousal cycle. A couple who take time and have the patience to truly recognize and accept this will not fall into the sort of trap that is waiting for those who make erroneous assumptions.

DRIVES AND DESIRES

*We all have a sex drive even if all it amounts to is masturbation
a couple of times a year. For many couples the problem is
matching their drives and coping with the difficulties that arise
when mismatching occurs. Fortunately, there are several
methods for coping with sex drive problems and professional
help is not usually necessary.*

Whilst it is probably true to say that most of us unconsciously choose a partner who has much the same level of sex drive as ourselves there *are* some differences between these drives, if only from time to time, in even the best relationship. It has been suggested that we all have somewhat different levels of sexual desire. Indeed, many of my patients assure me that this is the case, when they have problems in this area of their sexual lives. Clinical experience, however, suggests that this is a mistaken belief because even over quite a short time, someone who is supposedly 'frigid' or hardly interested in sex, can be transformed into a valued and exciting sexual partner.

The answer to this apparent contradiction is that we probably all have much the same level of sexual desire and that what makes the difference is the level of inhibition that prevents us from exhibiting our real sexual selves. People who appear completely passionless often turn out to have rich dream and fantasy lives but their unconscious tends to guard against this and as soon as anything that isn't 'nice' comes to mind, they find it impossible to translate their thoughts into actions.

Clearly we are all interested in sex to some degree – it is, after all, a part of our biology – but just how much is normal at any one time is difficult to know because we really have nothing to compare it with. There are numerous surveys available that show how much sex everyone else is having but such studies are often difficult to verify and even when they seem thoroughly reputable, people tend to look only at the best possible position for others and compare it with the worst possible position in themselves. 'Normality' when thinking about human sexual drive, is a range not a point, and all that can safely be said is that what is normal for you is normal for you.

Even within any one individual, sexual appetite varies quite a lot. Males are at the peak of their sexual appetite in their late teens and women at around forty. But whatever yardstick one uses there will always be someone you know who'll be bigger, better, longer, quicker, or slower and all such comparisons are fruitless. It is said that men want sex less as they grow older, but this is a gross generalization. Indeed some men in their sixties are just as active as they were in their twenties.

*This couple clearly have no problem with their sex drive. They are
attracted to one another and know how to arouse each other.*

DRIVES AND DESIRES

63

Notions of 'averages' in women are even more fraught with problems. There are women who can have twenty orgasms a day and others who are happy with none at all over a whole lifetime with a loving partner. Most women are more orgasmic during masturbation, as compared with intercourse, and any one woman's total sexual output through her life (intercourse plus self-produced orgasms) is probably more than a man's. A woman's capacity for sexual pleasure is almost limitless but her ability to exploit it is governed by her upbringing, her emotions, her personality style, her education, her partners, and her current circumstances.

There are many reasons for an individual's sex drive to fall or even fail. Drugs are a common cause. The Pill can produce a loss of drive in some women; sleeping tablets, steroids, some anti-high blood pressure drugs, and some anti-depressants can do so too; tranquillizers probably dampen more people's sex lives than does any other single external cause; alcohol can be a sex drive killer; and many illegal drugs take their toll. The most common psychological illness in the Western world is depression and a feature of the condition is a loss of sex drive. Depression usually calls for medical treatment with drugs or some kind of psychotherapy.

Serious physical diseases can reduce anyone's sex drive, as can physical or mental exhaustion. Many people overwork, exercise too little and sleep poorly and then wonder why it is that their sex drive is so low. Also, some people use their physical state to excuse themselves (quite unconsciously) from sex that they never really wanted anyway.

Unpleasant sexual experiences can destroy sexual drives. Some people have, or have had, such rotten experiences that they almost wish that sex did not exist. For such individuals, sex is just another wretched chore that they wish would go away. In some, a previous rape, sexual abuse as a child, or sexual assault is at the heart of such negative feelings towards sex, but in others the response is to something much closer in time. Guilt can be a major factor of sexual alienation, and those I see who are guilty, however unconsciously, often lack much sex drive for fear of doing something they would feel guilty about.

Some people are so unhappy with the state of their relationship that they close their minds to sex. After all, we feel most like having sex when things are going well. Many women tell me that they are not interested in sex because they have fallen out of love and men, too, are increasingly talking about such matters.

When some individuals have an affair they deny sex because of the guilt; the fear of discovery; the horror of an unwanted pregnancy or sexually transmitted disease; and so on. Yet others function best in illicit situations because sex within their one-to-one relationship is too cosy and 'nice' which is contrary to their unconscious views of what sex should be.

Quite a few women I see say that their sex drive is lost if their partner lets his standards of personal appearance slip. Husbands who smell of drink and overweight wives are two such categories that arise time and time again.

Lastly, many people find that their sex drive seems to vanish after a bad lovemaking experience inside or outside their marriage. A serious rejection can do it, as can an experience where one partner tries too hard to force their will, or particular desires, upon the other. A capricious wife or husband, or one who repeatedly turns the other down will ultimately destroy almost any person's desire, in time. Successful sex depends on predictability to some extent.

From this far from complete look at some of the causes of a loss of sex drive it is possible to see that the subject is highly complex. In fact, it may require all the skills of a professional to be able to interpret the true nature of the problem. I see many couples who come out with perfectly reasonable suggestions as to the cause of their problem yet, to the trained eye, they clearly cannot be the answer. Usually there is something much more subtle going on between them, with power battles, de-loving, parent-child games, and a host of other unconscious factors, some or all of which have to be resolved before true progress can be made.

Once medical causes have been ruled out there are several things that any couple can try for themselves. First, I always suggest stopping sex. Give it a rest and go back to loving courtship behaviour (see page 12). Next, sit down together and try to see what the causes might be. Even the far from exhaustive list, already mentioned, might give you some clues. If you find something simple wrong, there should be no difficulty in resolving it for yourselves but if you find yourselves slipping into deep confusing water, seek professional help.

The next step is to endeavour to make your lives more erotic. Increase your levels of sexual awareness. I find that couples enjoy this part best of all. Perhaps start to watch sexy films or videos together; purchase some erotic magazines or books and see what each of you finds arousing in the pictures and the text; share fantasies (see page 80); increase the erotic potential of your bedroom (see page 78); and take a sensual holiday (see page 32). All of these will raise the sexual temperature yet should not end in intercourse.

This approach might mean increasing your masturbation rate. Women, I find, do exceptionally well with this. As they engage in more masturbation they find that their sex drive with their partner returns.

The next step I suggest for any couple with problems is to really get to know about one another's genitals and their responses during arousal. Build up your sexual repertoire together but still refrain from sex. Discover all the ways possible to pleasure one another without having intercourse. This book is full of ideas. Read about sex and sexuality and learn more about the subject generally. This 'bibliotherapy' works wonders for many of the couples that I see.

Now you should be ready to re-start sex. Having made sex a priority in your lives, you will now find that any apparent mismatching between you has all but gone and that because you are both so much better attuned to each other's sexuality you will be able to talk through any real mismatching that might occur from time to time. Couples who have undertaken this sort of course with me say that they can tolerate even a quite severe loss of sex drive, for whatever reason, because they know that it will not be permanent and that they have all kinds of other ways of pleasing one another sexually and erotically. Such couples are still delighted with one another even when penetrative sex is off the agenda for some reason.

How much better this is, than to look outside your relationship for sex at the first sign of failure, dissatisfaction or loss of sex drive.

CASEBOOK

Over the years that I have been an 'Agony Uncle' I have received more letters about 'the sexual body' than any other single subject. Here are just a few of the more common concerns that people have.

My penis is only five inches long when erect and I'm sure that my wife will want another man because it is so small.
I bet she won't. There is no evidence that most women like longer penises as opposed to shorter ones – though, of course, there are bound to be some who do. What most women say is that it is what their man does with his penis that is more important. When women *do* stipulate the sort of penis they like, it is often thickness that is talked of rather than length.

My breasts are very small and I know my husband is a big boobs man. What can I do to overcome this problem?
First of all you could show him that small though your breasts are they are still highly erotic and give you a lot of sexual pleasure. Teach him how best to caress them so that you can both enjoy your breasts. Few men can resist this and it shows him that, contrary to adolescent fantasies and the 'girlie magazine' model, women with small breasts can make very sexy partners.

Next, how about helping him with his desire for big breasts, through fantasy? Whisper in his ear about a big breasted woman, next time you make love. Take him through a whole erotic story with a big-busted woman as the heroine.

Make the most of what you do have by dressing to show your breasts off and support them with good, flattering bras.

Lastly, and only even give this a thought if your small breasts are a concern to you as well as him – how about talking over the matter with your doctor? He could suggest a plastic surgeon if you are really serious. I have seen several women whose sex lives have benefited from a breast enhancing operation.

I have a lot of pubic hair that spreads onto my legs but my fiancé wants me to shave it all off. Would this be OK?
It is certainly safe to do so if it seems a reasonable action to you. How about going for a less drastic first step? Either you or he could trim your hair so that it is very short and then one of you could shave or depilate your bikini line neatly. Some couples find that shaving the area around the vagina, perineum and anus is also highly erotic. In this way when the woman is standing up with her legs together her pubic hair looks fairly normal, if short. Yet when she opens her legs for sex from halfway down her labia she is totally smooth.

Many women quite like the idea of being smooth in this area, especially if it excites their man but they don't want to be totally hairless when swimming, or changing for sport in the company of others. Practical problems such as barber's rash can be overcome with the use of an antiseptic cream.

I have had four children and fear that my vagina is too flabby for good sex. What could be done about it?

Quite a lot. First of all though, who says that it is too flabby? You might be making a fuss over nothing if your partner has not complained. If either of you *do* think it is too lax after the babies, you could try doing some pelvic muscle exercises. Sit on the toilet when you next want to pass water and teach yourself how to stop and start the flow just by contracting and releasing your pelvic muscles. Practice until you can stop and start the flow at will, time after time. Now you can contract the very same muscles when you are not on the toilet, perhaps travelling to work or waiting in a queue.

Put a finger inside and feel the muscles contract and then when you think you have strengthened them sufficiently insert a pencil (blunt end) into your vagina and grip onto it with your vaginal muscles as you try to withdraw it with your fingers. When you can hardly pull it out you have achieved success.

If things are really floppy or you have anything 'coming down', do see your doctor.

We have been married for two years but my vagina makes the most alarming noises when we have sex. What could it be?

These noises are coming from air that gets trapped in your vagina as you make love. Don't worry about it because it can do you no harm. The penis cannot force the air anywhere inside you.

In certain lovemaking positions air trapping is more likely than others. Some women say that all-fours positions are worst in this respect.

Change positions and see if this cures it. If not, just make a joke of it. After all, it is not a serious problem.

We have a super sex life yet my guy still reads girlie magazines. Why on earth does he do it when he has me?

Please don't worry about it. Men like to look at women without their clothes on and the reverse is often true as well. Men are highly 'turned on' by looking and most men say that however good and rewarding their relationship, they still like looking at other women's bodies. I know that you see these pictures as some sort of threat but they are not in reality. He has you and you say that sex is good for you, so why complain? Perhaps he fantasizes about what the girls would be like as sex partners but with some careful sharing about this you might be prepared to offer him what he thinks *they* would.

One of my outer lips hangs down much lower than the other and my inner lips are much bigger than most women's. Could this have come about because I masturbate?

It is highly unlikely. We are all made differently, if within the same overall pattern! The size and shape of women's genitals are very variable indeed, much to the surprise of many men. There is no evidence that masturbation does anything harmful to the shape or size of a woman's genitals unless, of course, you are doing something strange to them at the same time. Please don't concern yourself any more about it.

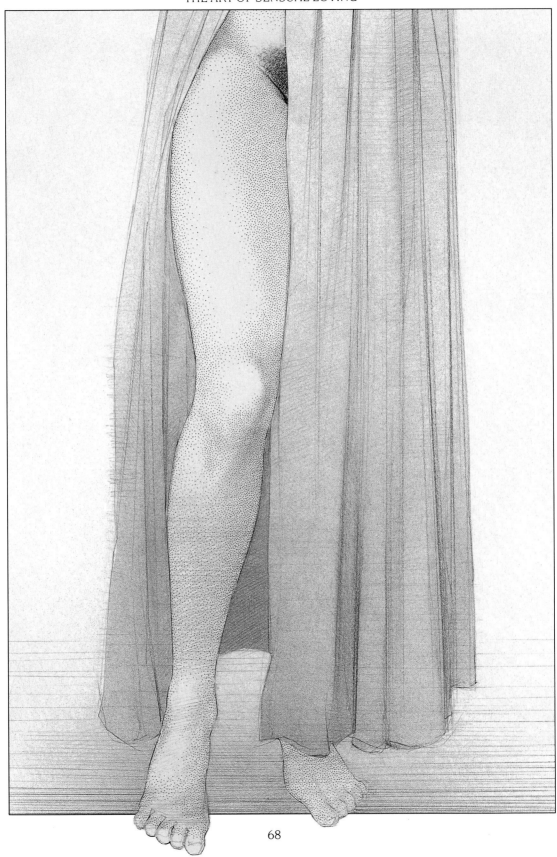

CHAPTER FOUR

SETTING THE SCENE

For the couple who both love one another and are lovers
the scene is almost permanently set for making love
whether or not this includes any sort of genital activity.
Against this background then, they play, copulate, and
have intercourse. We shall look in this chapter at setting
the scene for the romantic and sexual life in a way that
makes any sensual, sexual and erotic activity more
rewarding and pleasurable.

MAKING LOVE ALL DAY

With the emphasis placed on genitality today, many couples forget that setting the scene for such activity can be every bit as enjoyable as 'real sex' itself. Many people start off their married lives being very loving, close, and romantic but as the years tick by and perhaps pressures start to bear down upon them, things change, usually for the worse.

To me the term 'making love' means an ongoing expression of my love for my partner, not something that involves genital activity alone. It is a pity that most couples think of making love in a rather restricted way and then wonder why it is that they gain so little benefit from it. In a sense, all life between a loving pair of lovers is a form of foreplay to intercourse. But having said this, actual intercourse, or even copulation, takes up a tiny part of our lives together. By my definition, the rest of the time can still be devoted to 'making love', which is why I have called this chapter 'making love all day'.

Such ongoing lovemaking sets the scene for all loving and caring behaviour between a couple. It is a way of life rather than an event – and enhances a couple's value to one another hour by hour, day after day. Everything a couple do, even when they are not together physically, can still be a way of showing their love for one another. The man at work can make his work, however dull or boring, an offering of love to his partner; he is celebrating their relationship through his production of wealth for his family, or perhaps specifically for his partner. Clearly, a woman who works can do the same thing. A woman who is a mother, spending her time mainly at home looking after children can similarly celebrate her love for her man in the way she cooks, looks after the home, and cares for their children. Indeed, many women have told me how loving these activities feel, not just for them and the people involved but as a part of their whole 'lovableness'.

A couple who live like this might not actually have intercourse very frequently but they are in touch with one another all day, every day, through this kind of implied sexual bond – one that is largely spiritual. They are on the same wavelength, constantly attuned to one another's sexual, emotional and spiritual needs. Such a couple share a mutual private language; they exchange their thoughts easily, may even know what each other is thinking, and 'know' as if by some sixth sense, when one partner wants intercourse or any other genital activity.

When two people first meet they are two distinct individuals but as they mature together over the years they become more closely attuned to one another if they live in the way I am suggesting, until they become 'one body' in the Biblical sense of the phrase. The marriage now takes on a personality of its own. It is like a third party living with them under their roof. They are still themselves, of course, as unique individuals with their own interests, friends, hobbies, loves and hates – nobody takes anybody over – but the bond that they share, called their marriage, unites them in an ever-increasing way as the years go by. This might sound rather fanciful but it is real for many couples.

It is easy to see, bearing all this in mind, why it is that divorce can be so terrible. Indeed, why it actually kills some people, albeit slowly. Some have called divorce a 'living death'. Something of each of us dies when we divorce and in a couple who have enjoyed a good marriage at some stage, the death of the marriage itself is what they mourn, whatever they think about the other partner at that particular time.

Making love all the time as a backdrop to intercourse is often not easy; so how can it be done with any success? There are numerous ways and each individual couple will find that they discover their own path to success. Having said this, there are several tried and tested methods that seem to help and we shall look at a few here.

Many people I see have such poor opinions of themselves that it is hardly surprising that they feel unlovable, unworthy, and unattractive. The first thing they need to do is to improve their self-image if they are to consider themselves worthy of being loved by their partner.

A good place to start is to look at your appearance. Have you neglected your looks? If so, have a new look at your clothes and general appearance, perhaps with some help from a trusted friend or a professional. Have you put on so much weight that you do not look good in any of your clothes? If so, try a diet, join a slimming group, or seek professional help if you think the causes cannot be simply dealt with. Is your job boring? Change it if at all possible. Be brave, try not to be apathetic and claim that there is no alternative. Many people tell me that their awful job makes them feel worthless and it is my experience that a change of job can bring about all kinds of benefits to a relationship. Once you are released from your rut your self-esteem returns very quickly. Taking up a new hobby or developing new interests can help a lot too.

Are your family or children a cause of depression? Have you got money worries? Are you concerned about your health? Seek professional help to sort these things out, so that your life becomes less stressful, more rewarding and most important of all that you feel you can resume charge of it again.

At the same time, reconsider your life style. Most of us are so busy that we devote far too little time to ourselves and our relationship and then wonder why we cannot, as I suggest, make love all day. Many couples I see, especially younger ones, are so busy making money that they have almost no time to make love, in or out of bed. I get them to stop the clock every week and make time for themselves in their diaries, or filofax! This form of discipline improves matters very quickly and they start to give their relationship the priority it deserves.

Another problem I often encounter is the couple who cannot create a state of 'lovemaking' together because they are together too much and do little or nothing as individuals. We look at this problem in more detail on page 31. We all need to think of ourselves as unique, valued individuals, not only as half of a pair. By doing things on our own we bring seedcorn into the relationship, where it can be sown to grow for our mutual benefit. Far too many couples believe that this seedcorn should only come from within the relationship.

Once you have started to evaluate your life and physical appearance you will already start to feel better. Next, consider your diet and the amount of exercise you take. Eating healthily can make a great difference to how you feel within yourself. I have seen many individuals blossom on a large-dose, multi-vitamin, multi-mineral preparation that I prescribe. Years of poor eating and hastily consumed junk food has reduced their nutritional status to the ridiculous. After a month or two on high doses of vitamins and minerals, together with some recommended sensible changes in their eating patterns, such individuals feel better in themselves and note an increased interest in their sexual partner.

Exercise can make a tremendous difference to how we feel. Try to establish a routine of hard physical exercise, other than sex, at least three times a week. This helps in keeping slim, tunes up the muscles for sex, makes you feel better generally, and improves your body shape and contours. All of which makes the average person feel better in themselves and thus more lovable and 'worthy' for their partner.

Sleep is an often overlooked area. Seriously consider your bed, and if it is too small, too soft, or in any way unsuitable, get rid of it and obtain a new one. If this is too expensive, simply get a new mattress. Look at ventilation, the clothes you wear in bed (if any), the way you heat the room in winter, and so on, until you have dealt with any causes of disturbed sleep because to wake in the morning refreshed is most important.

The next step I suggest to people is that they make time to pleasure themselves physically, whether or not this results in masturbation. From time to time, put an hour aside to have a long bath, to soak and massage yourself sensually, and then to go to bed and caress yourself lovingly, perhaps to orgasm if that suits you. Keep making friends with your own body, re-acquainting yourself with what feels good, and luxuriating in it. Acknowledge both the good parts and the bad parts of your body and take a real pleasure in both. You do not have to have a perfect body to be attractive. Be realistic about what you cannot change, yet be prepared to change the things that you can. Concentrate on your good points and put the bad ones into perspective.

This making time to pleasure yourself should mark the start of making time to do the same with your partner. A person who feels that they are too unimportant to do such things will hardly ever, in my experience, think of themselves as valuable

Erotic games such as this keep lovemaking at the top of a couple's agenda. Her creativity and his delight keep the goodwill bubbling just beneath the surface. As a result, rows are few and sexual delights numerous.

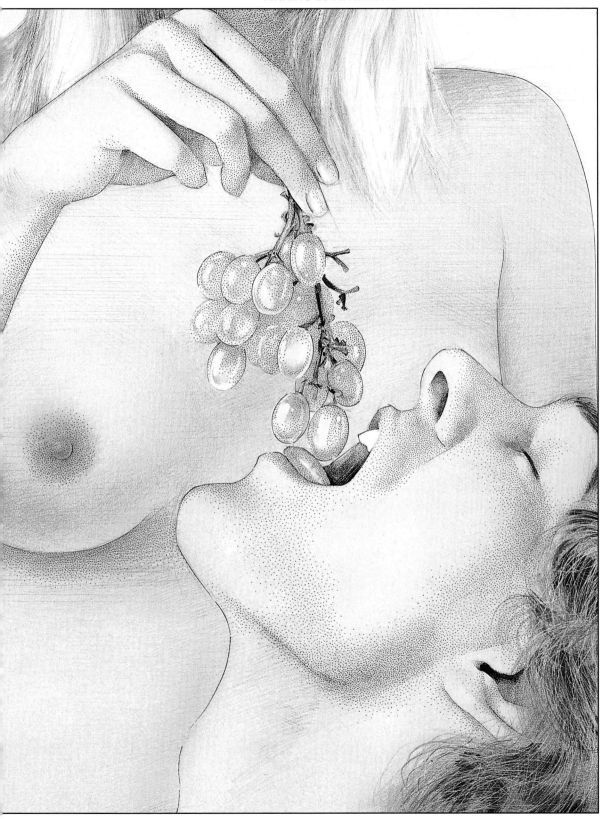

to their partner. Most people take us at our valuation of ourselves. Taking time for yourself to perhaps have a bath, to rediscover the pleasure of your own body, if you are a woman to make up carefully, to do your hair well, to show some respect for your body's nutrition, shape and style, makes it more likely that you will be able to do the same for your partner. Not only will you now feel more lovable and worthwhile in yourself but you will appreciate your partner in this way as well.

An important part of this learning about oneself involves becoming a real expert on your own sexual responses. Most of us learned to masturbate rather secretively and hastily during our childhood or adolescence and, as a result, have possibly got into bad habits that have remained with us into adulthood. Many such habits serve us unfavourably in our one-to-one relationship and could do with 'unlearning'.

I think it behoves us all to become totally confident with our own sexual responses so that when we share them with our partner in intercourse or foreplay we do so from a position of strength and knowledge.

As an extension of the personal time to caress your body and to pleasure yourself physically, return to the beginning and explore your own genitals and their responses. Try out new sensations, perfect your old techniques, work with new fantasy material, try to slow down or speed up your orgasmic cycle (whichever is appropriate), and generally enrich your personal sexuality. Not only is this an investment for your relationship but much more importantly, it gives you the peace of mind that comes from valuing your own sexuality *for yourself* and not just in the context of your relationship. This can lighten or remove the pressure from the genital side of your partnership because you will know that you can satisfy yourself well.

A man who does this will usually find that he wants sex less with his partner but this need not mean that he does not pleasure her in some other way. A woman pleasuring herself, however, usually finds that her whole sexual thermostat is set higher and indeed, that she wants more sex than usual. For this reason I encourage my female patients who are having problems coping with their body image, arousal or sexual performance, to masturbate very frequently. It is as if their own valuation of their sexuality raises their personal expectations that their partner will be equally delighted – as so often he is.

A natural extension of this stage is for you both to make sensual massage a regular part of your loving life together. I have found that this alone can increase the lovemaking that goes on between couples – and I do not mean intercourse. Learning to pleasure one another without sex having to follow is a definite investment for the future. It is highly enjoyable as well.

Next, you should start to build up your communication skills together. This is the subject of a whole book in itself but the following guidelines should help somewhat although they focus mainly on verbal communication.

Firstly, keep 'no go' areas to a minimum. Much disharmony between couples results from the raising of issues in life that are so tricky that they become like mines in a minefield. A couple with many such mines, or no-go areas, dare not communicate anything of much importance because as soon as they do, they tread on a mine and the relationship explodes. It is hardly surprising then, that such couples say little, especially about the things that really matter in life. Some examples of such no-go areas might be her breasts, his impotence, her mother, the children's schooling, her job, his drinking, and so on. Obviously no two individuals can agree about everything but a good friendship should be able to withstand quite a lot of disagreement. After all, there are no absolute answers to most things in life and one person's view should be valued as much as another's. Many no-go areas occur because so many men are brought up to think of women as being completely different from themselves – almost from another planet. This, such men argue, makes women 'impossible' to deal with.

None of this misunderstanding is necessary in a loving relationship. Take one no-go area at a time, perhaps write letters to each other about the subject and exchange them. I find this works well. Then follow this up with a chat in a private place, away from home, on neutral ground. Keep strictly to the subject in hand and do not wander off at a tangent or try to include all the wrongs of the world – or the relationship. Once you have managed to eliminate one no-go area it becomes a lot easier to discuss others. If, however, things get really complicated, seek professional help.

The second thing to remember is that your partner is probably your best friend and that it is wrong to expect him or her to bear the brunt of your own frustrations just because they are handy. There is a limit to what any of us can endure and if you have a frustration outside the relationship try to resolve it with whoever is involved rather than punishing your partner for it, however unconsciously. Be terribly careful of dangerous phrases such as, 'How could you understand, you are only a woman?; or, 'What sort of a man do you call yourself?' Such comments are deeply wounding and can stick in the memory. They badly damage day-to-day lovemaking. In fact, a few such comments made in anger or frustration can take weeks of loving behaviour to mend, and some are never repaired.

By all means argue but do not let arguments develop into rows. Try to argue constructively and keep to the point. If you wander from the subject, the whole relationship can soon be thrown into the discussion and one partner usually takes offence and storms out or ends up sleeping in the spare room. Try to have your arguments in the daytime, not just before you go to bed at night when you are tired out. Women complain bitterly that their men do not let them express their true feelings or that they do not feel understood by their partner. If you are a man reading this book, try much harder to allow your partner her say; give her time without interrupting, and really make it clear that you have understood what she said. The trouble with much arguing between couples is that although the 'receiver' may *hear*, he or she may not be *listening*. Try to train yourself into the habit of what is called reflective listening. Confirm what you think your partner's concerns are by restating them in your own words, just to see that you have understood exactly what he or she is saying. This not only shows that you are really listening but immediately clarifies the points and makes the speaker feel understood.

When one of you has had their say the other can follow. After this, compare notes and see what you *can* agree on. I find that making couples write down a summary of points that they have agreed on works very well. It is a source of constant interest to me to see how many couples start off seeming to be at each other's throats only to finish, in a therapy session at least, with far more common ground and points of agreement than they would have thought possible. This is very encouraging and supports my view that the process should be repeated at home. It works.

The next thing to bear in mind when communicating, especially about sex, is that it is all too easy to make assumptions about our partner based on ourselves. This means that we, often quite unconsciously, imagine that our 'nice' partner would not do certain things or, on the contrary, that 'because he is a man' he would do other things. We all make the mistake of thinking, and often saying, 'If you really loved me you would/wouldn't do X, Y or Z,' whereas our partner does not see either X, Y or Z as having anything to do with love at all. We are all brought up to see various sorts of behaviour as acceptable or unacceptable in varying degrees and we tend to assume that our partner shares these expectations, whether or not they really do apply.

This reveals just how vigilant we have to be if we are to stop ourselves from making harmful assumptions about our partner based on our childhood or our previous relationships. Focussing on our partner as a unique individual helps greatly but we need to be especially careful, for silly generalizations can creep into even the most loving of conversations.

Another helpful rule when communicating about anything, not just sex, is to refrain from making threats. Never threaten your partner. It is hurtful and damaging and your bluff just may be called one day. A major problem occurring when threats are being made is that the person doing the threatening often finds that they have based their evidence on erroneous assumptions. I find this situation crops up a lot in marital work. When reality dawns on the person concerned, threats are no longer necessary and he or she then feels rather foolish. Even if your partner does respond to a threat they will hardly feel good about it and will soon find themselves harbouring resentment. The seeds of long-term marital disharmony are then sown.

Lastly, try never to punish your partner. Many couples deliberately or unconsciously punish their partner and in some relationships this can become a damaging circuit. Sex suffers, housework and childcare are neglected, and the quality of life quickly spirals downwards. Most loving couples have learned from experience that such warring episodes are so damaging that they must resolve them early before they get out of hand.

Of course, there are many many other important things of which to be aware when communicating about issues that matter, and especially about sex, but a couple that bears these few points in mind will not go far wrong.

Even the couple who communicate well and are quite open about matters of concern, will still find that occasionally they need to spend time together, alone, to recharge their emotional and physical batteries if they are to remain loving and intimate day after day, year in, year out. There is no better way that I know of achieving this than the sensual holiday. This is discussed on page 32.

A couple that has worked at their relationship in the way outlined in this chapter soon start to feel like romantic teenagers, yet they are also perhaps responsible parents, workers, capable adults, and take an active part in society.

During their day-to-day lives they miss no opportunity to kiss and cuddle one another; they touch a lot; they tell each other sweet nothings; they compliment one another rather than criticize; they never forget anniversaries or birthdays; they never attack one another's personalities; they are aware of one another's moods; and they 'know' what the sexual temperature is at any time.

If one partner does not want sex he or she will relieve the other so that they are not left feeling frustrated. They know the difference between copulation and intercourse (see page 34); never force one another to do sexual things that either is unhappy with; and they do not interpret differences of opinion or sexual preference as a sign of unloving behaviour. Sexual failure or disappointment is easily coped with because against their loving background such problems are seen for what they are and treated accordingly.

It is interesting that in good relationships where couples are making love in this way much of the time, sexual failures and disappointments are treated with scant regard. Both my own clinical experience and other, formal studies have found that those who have a 'happy' marriage, as rated by themselves, are much less likely to see sexual failures, performance troubles, and arousal difficulties as 'problems'. Indeed, the vast majority of such difficulties never get taken to a professional, because the relationship is working so satisfactorily on other levels that it does not seem necessary.

Whilst it would be quite wrong of me to suggest that sex problems occur only in unloving and unsatisfactory relationships, it is certainly true that a making-love-all-day relationship does not rate such problems to be nearly as important as do less satisfactory relationships. It is always said that there are more sex problems around than there used to be but I believe that there always have been plenty of sexual 'colds and 'flu' around and that good, loving relationships have survived them because their marital immune system was so effective. What I believe we are now experiencing is a widespread sort of 'marital AIDS' in which many couples' immune systems are so poor that the relationship dies at the first sign of sexual 'dis-ease'.

Most of us marry with good intentions but over the years things can slip and the relationship can become impoverished rather than enriched. If we manage to achieve a worthy sense of self-love we are in a position to love our partner *for themselves* – not as an extension of ourselves. We are also, through developing insight, able to stop projecting our own dissatisfactions and personality short-comings onto our partner as if they were their problems. In short, by taking responsibility for ourselves, we allow our partner to be truly themselves and thus more free to be loved. This kind of growth takes time and a considerable amount of effort but it is well worthwhile because as we change in our understanding and behaviour, our relationship can change too. Change is usually painful, even if the outcomes appear to be positive in the long run. Making love all day helps a couple cope with such change and growth.

Many couples with whom I discuss all this think that it sounds something of a dream that is unlikely to be achieved. Indeed, for many it *is* difficult. But in my personal and clinical experience there is no substitute for it. To paint the sexual scene, the canvas on which it is to be created needs to be in as good a condition as possible. Only by making love all day can we hope to achieve this.

CREATING A ROMANTIC BEDROOM

Most couples sometimes make love in places other than their bedroom as we shall soon see, but most sex still takes place there. It is rather sad that so few people have truly given their bedroom, which ought to be their 'love nest', the consideration that it needs. In this section I suggest how to put that right.

The average couple's bedroom is somewhat less than romantic but there are several ways of improving things at relatively little cost and effort.

Be sure that you have chosen the best bedroom, with lovemaking in mind Most couples choose the largest bedroom in the house, but if it is possible to select a bedroom next to a room that is not always used then this would be ideal, from a soundproofing point of view. Most modern houses are very poorly soundproofed so you might want to improve this by lining the walls that adjoin other bedrooms with some board or dense fabric. Good thick curtains and a carpet also help to deaden sound. It is worth taking the trouble to be aware of sound because it can be very inhibiting to have to behave in ways that do not disturb those in adjoining rooms.

If at all possible, try to have a shower or bathroom adjoining your bedroom. A wash basin will suffice, but being able to shower or bathe together adds a pleasant dimension to an evening's lovemaking. It is also nice to be able to walk around naked without intruding on others in the house.

Lighting is very important. Try to have lighting that can be dimmed, or several small lights, perhaps at the bedside, that enable you to create a low level of light when required. For a really romantic evening use candles carefully placed on secure candlesticks.

Adequate warmth is a very important requirement in a bedroom. In some colder countries, the temperature of the bedrooms is kept so low that for much of the year only the most determined of couples can enjoy the sensual preliminaries to sex. If you have central heating the room will have a certain background heat much of the time. But in addition to this it is vital to have a fan heater to be able to warm the room up quickly before you intend to have sex. Start the heater at least half an hour before you want to use the room. Sensible draught-proofing and heavy curtains will also help.

Obviously the bed is a central feature of the sexy and inviting bedroom. Obtain the largest bed you can afford and have room for. The mattress should be firm for lovemaking and this is usually regarded as best for sleeping too. If the mattress is too soft, the woman's pelvis can sink into the bed and make penetration difficult and even painful.

Some couples like to dress up their bed to make it more romantic. An overhead canopy, a pretty bedcover, or even a four-poster can help to add a special touch to bed-time and lovemaking. Silk or satin sheets are the most sensuous and sexy choice but are impractical for laundering. They are also expensive to buy so most people settle for polyester-cotton sheets which, whilst not very sensual are at least practical. Duvets or quilts are probably the most practical for lovemaking though some people like to be tucked up in sheets and blankets. A few extra pillows can be useful for certain lovemaking positions.

If you have sufficient room, another piece of furniture worth acquiring is a chair. This should be firm and upright, without arms so that it can be straddled. A chaise longue is for real experts. I suggest keeping the floor as clear as possible so that you have enough room to lie down together to massage one another or even to make love. A fitted carpet, however inexpensive, is a good investment.

If you like sex toys and erotica, have a special drawer or cupboard that you can lock to keep prying eyes and fingers out. Erotic pictures can help to create a sexy mood but need to be fairly subtle and sensitive if others come into your bedroom.

Some people like to watch themselves or their lover in a mirror as they make love. This can be achieved by having mirrored door fronts on your wardrobes or even a free-standing mirror. This simple sort of voyeurism is exciting for some people but actually puts others off as it reveals how fat their bottom is or how silly they look when making love. Try it to see for yourself.

With the prices of electronics falling, some couples find that they can afford a second television and video for their bedroom. Whilst TV in bed is not conducive to sex in normal circumstances, if it is used for showing sexy films it can enhance your sex life. Do be careful that a television does not intrude into, or dominate your bedroom.

A box of paper tissues is an essential item for any bedroom table. A woman can use them after sex, so that she doesn't have to get up to wash. The man can have one to wipe his penis; they are handy for removing semen from the mouth after oral sex if the woman does not like to swallow it; and they can be very useful if the woman is menstruating.

Lastly, what about smells? Get some room perfume, perfumed candles, fresh, fragrant flowers or joss sticks to enhance the mood and make your bedroom pleasant to enter.

Creating the mood of your bedroom clearly involves more than the basic furniture you put into it. Take time to plan your bedroom together as an act of love. Try to please one another in choosing the decorations and even perhaps in the practical effort of renovation.

After all, it is *your* personal room together, your private retreat from the world, a place perhaps just to read in or to do something other than make love, a space of your own that enables you to be together, away from the troubles of the world.

In the hurly-burly of everyday life many couples find that making time and space for themselves can be almost impossible. If you have a bedroom that beckons, you will quite naturally want to spend time in it together. As you progress through your sexual career or marriage together, you may want to modify your bedroom to suit your current love-life style. Such alterations will simply reflect the more profound changes that are occurring in your relationship as it matures.

SHARING FANTASIES

Sharing fantasies is a wonderfully intimate way of coming to know and better understand one another's sexuality. Of course, it needs to be done sensitively and with love but if it is it can be one of the best possible ways of growing together sexually.

As any article on the subject in a woman's magazine will tell you, dreams and fantasies reveal much about our unconscious minds. Indeed, nowhere is this more true than on the subject of sex. Given that most of us find it difficult to communicate well about our real sexual needs and desires, even if we are consciously aware of them, and often we are not, sharing fantasies is an excellent way of getting to know one another better.

Each of us has a unique sexual personality – called our sexuality – and we are aware of some of it but not all. There are all kinds of inexplicable needs, desires, tastes, and fantasies that can come to mind either when alone masturbating; in our dreams or daydreams; or even when making love. Because we have been taught to restrain such thoughts, many of them are stifled and remain in our unconscious permanently. Yet they do not go away, they are always there, ready to be used for good or evil inside or outside our relationship. Therapists use this sort of information to learn more about an individual's unconscious in order to understand the person better than would otherwise be possible.

But sharing fantasies is not as easy as it might sound and before attempting to do so it is essential to be sure of your motives. This can be difficult. There is only one valid reason for sharing fantasies and that is to enrich and improve your relationship. Revealing things on the basis that, 'This is how I am and you'd better know it and deal with it', is not loving and can even be manipulative or intimidating.

The watchword when sharing fantasies is caution. If in doubt, keep your mouth shut and when you do say something be especially attentive to your partner's reaction. Just because something seems perfectly normal and acceptable to *you* does not necessarily mean that it will be the same for your partner. As a result, rather than opening up a subject of importance to you both, in reality you may have closed the door, perhaps for months or years. This makes caution vital if you really want to advance your relationship.

Another thing to remember is that once your partner knows something he or she cannot 'unknow' it. This in itself can bring new problems. A patient of mine had the fantasy of being tied up and taken forcefully by several men at once. She shared this cautiously with her man only to find that he was horrified. He now was faced with the dilemma of finding out how he, a sensitive, decent, loving man could fit himself into the sex life of such a 'sex maniac', as he put it.

Perhaps here I should challenge the myth that all fantasies are unfulfilled wishes or needs. This is not true. Many people have fantasies that, given the possibility, they would avoid like the plague in real life. The woman quoted

This began as her fantasy but on sharing it with her lover she discovered that it was one that he enjoyed too. This is a common experience for couples who are well matched.

above is one example. This is part of the success of fantasies – they are not necessarily meant to be acted out. Indeed some people say that when they do try to act out their favourite fantasy it backfires on them by being a disappointment. Remember that the essence of fantasies is that they are controllable by the one to whom they belong. In a fantasy the men or women are all attractive, sexually stimulating, and do exactly what the owner of the fantasy wants. This is highly unlikely in real life because the fantasy person would also have a will and sexuality of their own which they would want to impose on the individual. If the acting out is a disappointment then the individual may have lost something of real value because the fantasy itself may now become redundant.

Some men, and not a few women, say 'If you really loved me you'd do . . .' (whatever it is). This puts considerable pressure on the receiver to either make things happen, or appear to be unloving. Some people will even place their whole relationship in jeopardy given this pressure but this is usually a sign of a much greater problem. Generally the individual is, however unconsciously, trying to test the relationship but often the test is an unreal one because the other does not see that acting out a fantasy is any sort of test of their love. Thus sharing fantasies for the wrong reasons can be hazardous. For many couples, however, the greater problem is not sharing at all, for fear of being thought of as sex-mad, wanton, perverted, impossible to please, dirty, sinful, or just odd.

Sharing fantasies should obviously be done carefully. Choose your timing with care, preferably when you are both feeling very aroused. Suggest a small part of the fantasy, perhaps in a story form, and see how your partner reacts. This requires some bravery at first for fear of rejection, but bear in mind that marital and sex therapists often discover that couples have surprisingly similar fantasies but did not realize it until they shared them. This can occur because the couple are highly attuned at an unconscious level.

Starting off can be complicated because you may not have any idea about your partner's fantasies. Straight questioning can succeed in a frank and open relationship but many people find that careful observation works better, preferably over some time. Watch what your partner likes to read, what is exciting during films and videos, or whilst reading books and magazines. Having obtained some ideas, weave them into a fantasy story that you know will please and then try to get your partner to tell you what best affected them – if you have not already found out by their responses. This approach not only reveals existing fantasies and makes them easier to share but also creates new ones which can be personalized to you both during lovemaking.

Reading the sexy letters in erotic magazines is another good source of fantasy material. Once the suggestion has been made, if only by a magazine letter, even quite a shy partner will start to reveal things that would otherwise have remained unsaid. A little alcohol helps in this exercise.

A favourite with many of my couples is attempting the writing of a sex video outline. I ask them to create a 'script' for a really sexy film that they are to direct. It can contain anything they choose but it must be really stimulating for them. If both partners do this separately and then exchange scripts, they can learn a lot about one another's fantasies.

On occasions the sharing of fantasies really opens up a relationship. The woman who seems shy and inhibited can often reveal amazing fantasies and her partner sees her in a completely new light. The timid man who fantasizes about women raping him is probably unconsciously saying that he wants his partner to take the lead in lovemaking, if only from time to time. Such disclosures can prove to be an illumination in some troubled relationships. In fact, it is one of the most useful therapies that I employ in such situations. This honesty, perhaps after a whole lifetime together, can alter the position so dramatically that the couple see one another afresh and their sex life blooms as never before.

But just because something is revealed does not, as we have seen, mean that it should necessarily be acted out. Acting out, if done, should be tackled with caution, obliquely at first rather than bluntly. So, for example, a woman who is blatantly against anal sex in real life yet who actively fantasizes about it frequently, can be made love to in a rear-entry position on all fours while she fantasizes that her man is penetrating her anally. This might, if the couple feel safe with it, eventually lead on to incorporate true anal sex, but it might not.

Things which cannot actually be accommodated in fact can be created in fantasy by the loving partner. A man who has fantasies about a famous film star, for example, can re-live a sexual encounter with her in fantasy if his partner makes it real enough as she talks him through the fantasy as they make love.

A good game that works well is called 'whisper in the ear'. In this the woman (or the man if the game is being played the other way round) whispers in her partner's ear a story of great erotic delight. The secret here is to weave a story containing detailed elements of what you know best arouses your partner. By carefully specifying all the details you ensure that he or she receives the maximum pleasure from it. For this game to work best you will need to talk about the story afterwards at some stage to make sure you said the right things. Having said this, the average lover can discern fairly easily which elements of the tale are most arousing by monitoring their partner's sexual arousal carefully. Research for these stories will be done over a long period through vigilant awareness of what stimulates your partner in all kinds of settings in life. Once you find a really good theme that excites him or her, adhere to it adding only tiny variations because, as with masturbation, most people like the predictability of such arousing material. Some couples find that making themselves the subjects of the story works best.

The only real danger possible from this sort of sharing is if the fantasy is of someone else you both know. It is probably unwise to encourage your man to fantasize about the woman next door just in case fantasy, given a nudge, becomes reality. Similarly, I advise couples not to encourage one another's criminal fantasies – for example having sex with children.

Other simply 'odd' needs can, however, be very easily fulfilled in fantasy. Indeed, it is my experience, and that of many other therapists, that such fantasies can be extinguished with time, acceptance and care. They are often replaced with material that is more 'wholesome', especially if the partner provides all the right cues and helps with substitute material. For some people, fantasies in general or certain fantasies are so personal that they do not want to share them even with their beloved. This is fine. We all have our limits and certain fantasies seem to lose their power to help us if we share them. For some, a particular fantasy is like a sexual talisman that has to be used if they are to function well, or even at all. Perhaps for them to make such a fantasy public would rob it of its magic. Indeed, this is what some people have told me to be the case.

If you desperately want to act out a fantasy but your partner will not consent to participate, you may have a problem. I have suggested some ways around this but if they or something similar do not work be very wary about looking outside the relationship to fulfil your fantasy. Often such material acted out with a prostitute, or in an affair, falls far short of what was hoped for and you may have damaged your relationship by even looking outside it. Most loving partners can accommodate one another's needs, if only in fantasy. With some common sense, creativity, and love few people should have to remain with their needs totally unmet. The trouble with looking outside your relationship is that it is so easy to over-interpret the value of the fantasy being acted out that one can overlook the real value of the partner one already has. Because the new partner indulges your fantasies, it does not necessarily make him or her a better partner overall – in fact it can be almost impossible to make any rational decision on the matter, so heady is the brew.

One reason why many people do not dare to share their fantasies is that they fear they are the only ones who have ever had such an outrageous idea. This becomes really obvious when I am working with couples. The man on his own one week, will declare, with considerable fear and trepidation, some 'unspeakable' fantasy (probably shared by eight million others in the country), feel ashamed about it and ask me to be sure not to tell his wife. The wife had already, the week before, said the same thing about an almost exactly similar fantasy. Their faces, when they are both told of this situation, are a pleasure to see because not only do they realise that they have more in common than they thought but they are also not nearly as odd as they feared.

Common male fantasies involve famous public figures, specific women known by the man, doing familiar things with his partner, doing experimental things with his partner, homosexual fantasies, and many others. Female fantasies vary greatly but the most popular is about something they have done with their partner and especially enjoyed. This often involves the creation of a highly romantic scene, perhaps on holiday. Fantasies about someone they know or work with are common, as in men; famous males rank highly; homosexual fantasies are far more common than most people would imagine, as are fantasies involving animals. Being dominated, being a slave, being beaten or abused in some way is a very popular form of female fantasy as are many kinds of fantasy involving being made to have sex 'against her will'. Sex with more than one partner or with one's partner looking on while someone else makes love to them is also a common fantasy in both sexes.

Whatever your fantasy, be a little wary about how and when you use it, if your partner knows about it. For example, knowing that your favourite is about your previous lover and what he used to do with you is all very well and could even enrich your love life together but if your man is feeling low for some reason, or is experiencing any sexual difficulty, he could be thoroughly annoyed to learn that you were fantasizing about your ex-lover while he was making love to you. Declaring what your fantasies are when actually making love calls for some care but if you both tread carefully all but the most sensitive material can greatly help raise the sexual temperature. In fact, many female patients of mine have told me that they never have any more trouble with tired, worried, nervous, redundant, or whatever, husbands once they feed his fantasies or tell him what they are fantasizing about as they have sex. Such intimate revelations can revive even the most flagging sex drive. Indeed, many couples who use fantasy creatively find that they can act as personal sex therapists to one another. If sexual malfunctions and disappointments are dealt with in this way, professional help is usually not necessary.

For many people, listening to their partner's fantasy, especially when making love, is somewhat voyeuristic. With a fertile imagination, you can build on what your partner shares with you and make the whole sexual act possible when perhaps circumstances would have suggested that sex was 'off the agenda' for some reason, that day.

This sort of sex therapy can avert many minor failures, through checking any frustration before it occurs. Given that so many, especially male, sex problems arise from a fear of failure rather than the failure itself, any woman who can defuse such a problem early on has a valuable weapon against failure and disappointment.

Lastly, I would like to mention a few words about love. Many, women especially, think it unloving to hear their partner's fantasies or indeed to share their own. There is no absolute answer to this because we all have very different ideas as to what is 'unloving'. If you work, as I do, on the principle that anything that enriches and enlivens a couple's sexual life together can only be good, then sharing fantasies must be predominately good. It is loving in the most profound sense of the word, to know one another and be truly known and I encourage couples to see that by sharing in this way they are *more* likely to be loved, not *less*. A fear of being odd, of being unacceptable, or even unlovable, dominates many individuals in even quite solid relationships. In my view, sharing should be established during courtship so that we enter into a life-long relationship with honesty and not with all kinds of worries and fears looming in the background, ready to alarm or threaten us when we least expect, or want.

The sharing of fantasies is one of the most intimate and loving things a couple can do. Because of this it should not be undertaken lightly and is probably something we do only once or twice in a lifetime with someone we trust and who trusts us. Sharing fantasies can be very liberating, and builds trust between a couple in a way that few other activities can. 'Having sex' is easy by comparison, and as such, does not have the lasting value. True intercourse involves the sharing of everything about oneself as a part of total trust. I find that the sharing of fantasies is important in this context and am somewhat wary of the couple who will not do so. Often they need to work on their ability to be intimate, to share and to trust in many other areas of life before sexual fantasies can be safely shared.

CHANGING THE SETTING

*Although most couples make love in their bedroom many find
that a change of scene can make all the difference between
good sex and really adventurous lovemaking. With some
thought and creativity a new situation can also add a touch
of novelty and fun.*

The vast majority of lovemaking takes place in a couple's bedroom. Having
said this, my clinical experience and the results of many studies show that
most couples also enjoy making love in other places, if only from time to time.
Probably the most common places outside the bedroom are the living room,
the kitchen and the bathroom. I find that those couples who have sex in
different locations are more likely to be satisfied than are those who confine
themselves to their bedroom.

The appeal of places other than the marital bedroom is obvious. They are
somewhat 'naughty', being more public than the bedroom; the fear of
discovery adds to the adventure for many; we end up making love in varying
degrees of dress and undress which takes us back to our courting days; we
adopt new positions; and we can avail ourselves of the rather special facilities
that the particular situation makes possible. For example, making love in the
bathroom is, by definition, more sensuous if it involves the use of water; and a
passionate session one night in front of the living room fire has rather special
romantic appeal.

One of the joys of making love in new places is the spontaneity involved. For
the woman who comes home feeling really sexy to find her man getting the
supper ready, a spontaneous encounter in the kitchen can be a memorable
experience for both. Almost any occasion can be turned to our sexual
advantage if we start to think in this way. For instance, what starts off as a
rather boring job of repainting the spare room can soon, if the man takes his
top off and the woman perhaps wears only a shirt, turn into a much more
stimulating experience that results in sex among the paint cans.

Given that most couples tend to make love in the same place and even at
much the same time week-in and week-out, such spontaneous lovemaking can
really add spice to a relationship. Part of the success of such events lies in the
fact that one or other gets carried away with desiring their partner, and the one
who is desired really feels special. Sex that occurs almost by appointment in
the marital bed has a habit of becoming somewhat predictable and even
boring. Predictability and boredom will be banished if you are always on the
lookout for new locations.

Making love in the bathroom can unfold all kinds of new thrills. Make the
room warm, take the phone off the hook, lock the door, have some music
playing if you like it, and take things slowly. Start off by massaging one another
for a while out of the bath and then, once in the water, soap one another all
over, leaving the genitals till last. When you are washed, you can feed one

another with delicious fruits. Mango is one of the most sensuous and erotic fruits and much easier to consume in the bath! Perhaps also have a glass of wine or some other alcoholic drink to give to one another.

Rubbing one another's bodies with soap or a loofah can be a highly erotic and exciting piece of foreplay that might well result in actual intercourse. If you have sex in the bath be careful of soap getting inside the woman's vagina because this can cause irritation. Having said this, washing one another's genitals and bottoms can be highly erotic. Rear-entry positions work well in the bath and are a favourite for many in the shower. In many ways a shower is more sensuous than a bath, but given that the supplies of hot water are limited in most homes, it can be a more short-lived pleasure.

Relaxing afterplay is especially delicious in a bath and for the woman who is squeamish about her partner's personal hygiene, oral sex can take on a whole new meaning as she scrupulously prepares him. A few couples like to watch or listen to one another passing water as part of their bathroom sex.

Making love in the kitchen has a certain earthiness about it that appeals to some. The sheer urgency of such sex is usually the attraction here. Some highly inventive couples make use of kitchen implements to enhance their lovemaking and of course, fruits and vegetables are at hand for the man who likes to use them in his lover's vagina. Ice from the fridge can be a source of pleasure on the nipples or in the woman's mouth as she fellates him and for the adventurous couple the kitchen table is just the right height for him to stand comfortably and penetrate her as she lies back on the surface. Any remarks about how badly the kitchen ceiling needs repainting should be strenuously ignored!

Sex in the living room can be much like sex in the bedroom but the sofa and other furniture can offer delightful possibilities. Watching a sexy video can add spice to the occasion. Perhaps the biggest hazard with this location is remembering to be aware of discarded underclothes which could prove to be embarrassing when you next have visitors or your children discover them. Especially as you might have spent some time telling your family not to leave their clothes all over the house!

Even if you live in a rather cold climate, sex out-of-doors can be great fun. A lot of the pleasure revolves around the fear of being discovered but as I always point out to those who relish fresh air, do be sure that what you are doing cannot cause offence to others. Sex in public is illegal so be careful, even in your own back garden, not to offend other people.

Lovemaking out-of-doors has many attractions. The fresh air; the warmth of the sun; even the brisk cold in winter; the naughtiness; the unfamiliarity; the partial undressing; the replay of adolescent fumblings; and the sheer silliness of it; can all enhance arousal.

Of all the places to make love out-of-doors your garden is the most obvious setting because it is an extension of your home. Clearly, there must be sufficient privacy but even a cosy corner can be enough if you are discreet. Summer time is best and sex can easily follow massaging one another with suntan oil. For all but the most hardy, some sort of inflatable bed or groundsheet will be necessary.

Playing naked on a swing is fun. A good game is for the woman to sit naked on the swing with her pelvis well forward and for the man to kneel down in front of her so that with each gentle swing forward his mouth comes into contact with her vulva. Either of you can make the woman swing back and forth teasingly. As the level of excitement increases the man can penetrate the woman with his fingers and she can push the swing back and forth to work his fingers in and out of herself. It is but a short step from this to actually penetrating her with the penis as she swings to and fro.

This situation can be repeated with the woman kneeling up on the swing with her naked bottom enticing the man to enter her from behind. Such games can be enjoyed even more with both of you partially undressed.

Many couples like to chase one another, with the quarry teasing the hunter by removing a strategic piece of clothing, perhaps even leaving a trail for him or her to follow. This can be modified to create the game of chasing one another and on catching the prey removing a piece of clothing of your choice. Then the first person to be naked has to pay a forfeit of some kind to their partner. It is often fun to delay the payment as a sort of sexual 'torture'.

Making love in the garden offers all kinds of novel delights and has the already mentioned advantage of being a part of your own domain. You can easily run back inside the house to go to the toilet; to get a drink; to retrieve a forgotten contraceptive; to get some paper hankies; or whatever. Your garden can, if it is sufficiently private, become an extension of your bedroom, if only possibly, in the summer.

A great favourite for romantic fantasy is the beach. The rhythmic beating of the waves, the salty smells, the moonlight, and the warmth of the sand in the day, can all create and enhance a unique lovemaking adventure that lingers in the mind for years. Many couples have fond memories of seaside sex.

Sand does, however, create some practical problems for lovers. Combined with suntan preparations it can make a gritty mess that is anything but exciting, and making love at the water's edge can be a real misery if sand gets into the vagina or into the penis. Making love in deeper water can be highly arousing, though. Either the woman can lie back and cross her legs behind her lover's back as he enters her from in front, or she can stand waist high in the water and bend over to lie on it as he enters her from behind. A favourite position is to have the woman lie flat on her back floating so that her hips are at the level of his genitals. He now enters her and, holding onto her hips, guides her body onto his penis. If you are far enough away from people this is a game that can be played even if you are not totally alone in the sea. Be sure not to lose your bikini bottom in the process! As holidays are such an ideal time for couples to behave romantically and to experiment with new locations, seaside sex can offer much pleasure. However, when on holiday be sure not to overexpose yourself to the sun because a burnt skin combined with sunstroke are hardly conducive to a sexy time together. Be especially careful of topless

Partially undressed, this couple have created a loving moment in the kitchen after their guests have departed.

bathing and sunbathing because your nipples could get terribly sore and thus prevent many of your *normal* bedroom pursuits as well as any new ones you may have planned.

In some countries, people do not often have the opportunity to travel to a warm beach but usually the countryside is not far away and can be enjoyed as a part of their sex lives. Simply walking together in the countryside can be a powerful aphrodisiac. The fresh air, the freedom from other people, the birdsong, the smells of pasture and earth, can all contribute to making a country walk a very sensuous occasion.

Make love against a tree, lying in a meadow, or by a riverbank. The imaginative use of wild flowers can also enhance the occasion. A woman's cleavage can be the perfect place for a natural bouquet and once undressed how about adorning one another's pubic hair? Playing putting things down one another's clothes is silly but fun, as is retrieving them. How about massaging one another with fresh herbs or grasses? Just lying there in the sun in a secluded place can be close to a spiritual experience for some people.

If you are playing with natural 'toys' do be careful. Think twice before putting things into your lover's vagina and never, ever put anything into the penis. I have witnessed some tragic outcomes from this sort of 'nature sex'.

A good rug or groundsheet is almost essential for lovemaking in the countryside because the realities are that insects, prickly leaves and so on intrude on the most romantic of pleasures. How about combining a picnic with your lovemaking? The two can, of course, come together if you have any sense of playfulness. Yoghurt or cream can be dabbed onto her breasts or his chest ready for licking off, and retrieving soft fruits from his lap without the use of hands can provide a hilarious and arousing sensation for the man without his pants on. Having intercourse out-of-doors like this can be marvellous but it usually involves adopting new positions because of the hardness of the ground, and other practical considerations. Once you have made love it is wonderful to lie in one another's arms in the open air and just sleep or doze. Some couples like to move some branches and crawl in among the bushes so that they can remain totally undisturbed by passers-by even if they are asleep.

It is true to say that the chance element of being discovered is half the fun for many country lovers. There is something highly arousing about being involved in your own private world of sex and sensuality, perhaps not far from others who are unaware of your presence.

Lastly, do remember to clear up after your lovemaking. Paper hankies should be taken home, as should condoms. Cattle are notoriously curious and many irate farmers have experienced sick animals that have eaten condoms.

Making love in cars is a favourite of many young couples and takes most people back to memories of their courting days. However, doing anything in a *moving* car is madness. This applies particularly to the ridiculous practice of the woman who likes to fellate her man while he drives. Provided you have parked somewhere quite private you can enjoy yourself as far as the vehicle will allow. The trouble with many cars is that they are too small for really good lovemaking. Most couples find that the back seat is best with the front seats pushed as far forward as they will go. Estate cars are certainly more practical and obviously camper vans and larger vehicles provide much more scope. A patient of mine frequently has sex in his camper parked on a yellow line in the main road. The curtains are always drawn, he hastens to assure me.

Generally, in-car sex is pretty unsatisfactory. It is confined; highly restrictive except for oral sex; is suited only to quick copulation rather than true intercourse; and can soon generate muscle cramps.

Camping is a popular recreation that enables couples to enjoy many of the advantages of sex out-of-doors but without the disadvantages. Now you can have a proper mattress or airbed and relax in real comfort. Needless to say, in a tent there is a whole new dimension of privacy compared with true out-of-doors sex. The private world that you can create is also very cosy which adds to the romantic appeal. Do remember though that although you cannot be seen (unless you keep on your interior light!) you certainly *can* be heard, so be careful about noises that could offend other campers.

Boating can be fun for outdoor sex. It contains an element of danger and this always sets up a sexual scene well, but it also enables the creative couple to obtain some privacy, when perhaps they are afloat in an otherwise public park. If the woman is not wearing panties and sits opposite her man with her legs apart as he rows the boat the sexual temperature soon rises and he becomes bored with propelling the boat. They can, with some thought, seek out a shaded area under trees and, with the ever-present hazard of falling in, cuddle or caress one another quite intimately. Actually having sex in a small boat has its own delights and the bigger the craft the greater the potential. Even on a quite large boat sex has something of a magical quality that is quite different from being on land.

Many couples are excited by the thought of hasty sex in some sort of public place like a park, a bus shelter, an alleyway, or a piece of wasteground. The woman can prepare herself in advance by removing her panties and wearing only stockings and suspenders, and the man can refrain from wearing his pants under his trousers if he does not find it too uncomfortable. By lifting her skirt he can caress her vulva and vagina easily and she can unzip the fly on his trousers. If you let one another know your plans well beforehand this adds greatly to the anticipation of the event and anticipation is half the thrill, like most pleasures in life.

An amusing and erotic extension to any kind of planned outdoor sex is to take along a camera. Take it in turns to photograph one another but be aware that processing laboratories are unlikely to develop anything too explicit. Generally speaking, naked bodies are acceptable but erections or any sort of genital intimacy between a couple is not. Use polaroid films if the photographs you plan to take are too personal for the high street shop. A creative couple can make their own outdoor video, perhaps after some rehearsals.

Making love in places other than the bedroom can add spice and fun to even the best of love lives. With some preparation; care about privacy; advance planning and inventiveness, almost any couple can create an environment that will provide great fun at the time. Such 'events' will also ensure a really memorable occasion to perhaps recall in fantasy and with which to embellish their lovemaking in the future.

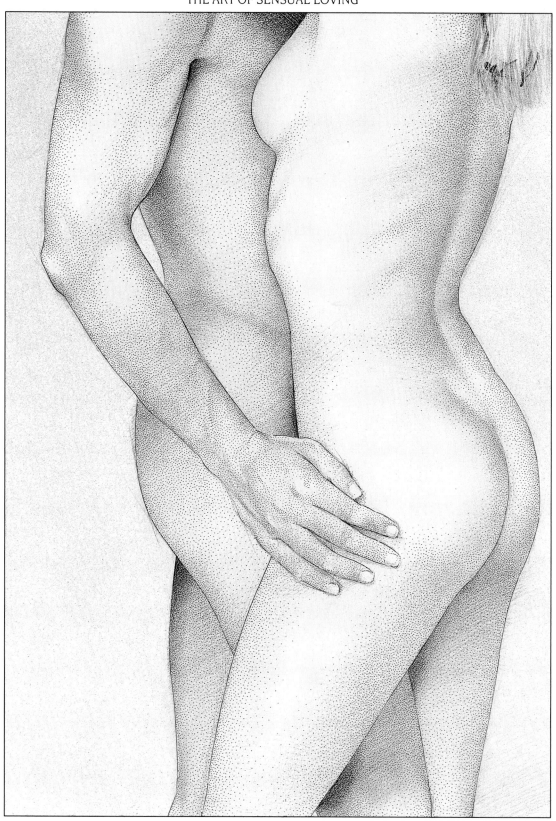

CHAPTER FIVE

MAKING LOVE WITHOUT INTERCOURSE

A loving couple who are in tune with one another's sexuality 'make love' through touch, gesture, and speech most of the time they are together – and even perhaps when they are not. This emotional, physical, and even spiritual communication generated between them can be far more important than are the relatively few moments that they spend having intercourse. In this chapter we look at making love without intercourse – the mainstay of a truly loving relationship.

SENSUAL COMMUNICATION

*The relaxing, soothing sensations created by a sensual massage
are a marvellous way of learning to communicate and share
without having sexual intercourse. Practising sensual massage
is not only pleasurable but helps to develop a closer,
loving relationship.*

Massage is simply a structured way of touching. There are many different methods, but here we shall look only at ways of touching that bring a couple closer together, enabling them to communicate and share emotionally, and even spiritually.

It is worth making sensual massage a regular part of your relationship because it encourages you both to spend time together; it costs nothing but time; it is not goal-centred to produce orgasm, unlike so much intercourse; it can be a fulfilling substitute for intercourse, or it can be a good addition to intercourse; and, of course, it is wonderfully relaxing.

Before you begin to massage your partner, try to create a quiet and loving environment. Take the phone off the hook; ensure that you will not be disturbed; dim the lights; warm the room; put on some music; prepare a firm, padded, comfortable surface on the floor; remove any jewellery and make-up; and undress as much as you feel at ease with. Ensure that your fingernails are clean and short and that your hands are clean. Because massage involves the skin, it is nice to bathe together first. In fact, your massage can begin in the bath or shower if you like.

There are very few precautions to bear in mind but it makes sense not to massage one another if either of you is not feeling well or is in an angry mood. This consideration is actually quite important because at the heart of sensual massage is the giving and receiving of vital energies from our bodies, and if we are unwell or angry we can adversely affect our partner. The only other precaution is that it is, of course, common sense not to massage someone who has a medical problem that might be aggravated by pressure.

The whole essence of sensual massage is that the 'giver' does exactly what is best for the 'receiver'. I say 'giver' and 'receiver', but in truth when a loving couple are massaging one another it is impossible to say who is giving and who receiving because it is a two-way process. The receiver is, in a sense, just as active as is the giver.

The main thing is for the receiver to be able to feel totally trusting, and completely relaxed, safe in his or her lover's hands. I always tell couples that I teach never to let one another down – and to treat each part of the body as if it were made of the most valuable porcelain.

Massaging, or communicating through touch, is a wonderful alternative to speech. Most couples feel that the only way they can communicate is to talk, but in fact most of us communicate far more by other methods, including, of course, our body language. By suspending speech almost entirely, as happens during a loving massage, the giver learns to interpret his or her partner from tiny tell-tale signs such as a little moan, a sigh, a slight appreciative body movement, and so on. This obviously takes some time to practise and in the early days it will mean sharing exactly how you feel as you receive. This should enable your partner to personalize what he or she does so that it produces the best possible sensations for you.

Sensual massage need not lead on to intercourse. In fact the best thing about it, according to many couples, is that it enables them to be loving yet not feeling that sex has to follow. Massage takes the pressure off many people who otherwise feel obliged to make every loving encounter end in sex. Of course, for some couples, the deep communication and pleasure involved *will* lead on to sex quite naturally, but it is sensible to come to an agreement in advance, and not indulge in any sort of genital activity. This means avoiding both the breasts and the genital areas. It is, after all, not meant to be sexually arousing.

You do not need much by way of equipment for a sensual massage. Some couples like to caress one another with a feather, some fur, silk or other materials they find sensuous, before starting the massage proper, but for most the hands are the only necessary tool. Use oil to lubricate the skin. Any oil will do but the best are almond, sunflower, safflower or coconut, and they are widely available. Aromatherapy oils smell delicious and have therapeutic effects in themselves. They can be diluted in a simple oil for everyday use.

Warm your oil beforehand in front of a radiator or in warm water, and use a bottle with a pump action dispenser or a nozzle, that allows you to squirt out just the amount you need.

Preparation before the massage is important. Calm your mind. Start with your partner lying face down, and cover them up with a large towel so that they can relax. A small pillow may help make things more comfortable for the receiver, and it is best to begin massage with the back, as we shall see.

Firstly, just kneel on the floor beside your partner and with one hand on the top of the back and the other at the top of the buttocks, simply hold this position for a while, breathing in and out together. This synchronized breathing helps to attune you to one another and is relaxing itself. Now, slowly and lovingly, remove the towel by pulling it down the back, to leave just the back area free to be massaged. You are ready to begin.

When applying oil to the body, put it first in your hand, never directly onto the skin just in case it is still cold and shocks your partner. Try always to keep one hand in contact with the receiver's skin to provide a sense of security and continuity. Apply oil to the whole area you intend to massage. Put on just enough to make it feel slippery but not so much that it runs all over the place, or feels so slippery that there is very little definite contact between your skin and the receiver's. A little practice and you will soon become expert at this.

Finally, if you are worried about expertise, remember that there is no set way to massage your partner. In general, it is always best to go slowly when massaging one another. Only experience will tell you what he or she best enjoys. At first, this will involve quite a lot of trial and error, but you will soon learn exactly what is best. It is then a matter of perfecting techniques and accommodating changing needs and tastes as your love life matures.

EASING BACK TENSION

How much of your partner's body you massage at any one sitting will depend on what you both want and how much time you have. Most people though, given a choice, say that they would like their back done. This is because the back, especially at the base of the neck, and the shoulders, is where many of us feel tension.

The back is a good place to start because it is relatively strong and so is less likely to be hurt as you get used to massaging your partner; it is large and responds to many different types of massage techniques; it is exceptionally relaxing and so prepares the receiver for other areas to be massaged; and lastly, because many people, even if they are long-term partners, feel easier about starting such an intimate process with the front of their body hidden from view.

*There are three good positions for massaging the back. You can sit or kneel at your partner's side; position yourself at his head with your knees either side of his ears; or you can sit astride his body at the hips being very careful not to put too much weight on him; **right**. This last position is exceptionally loving as it enables the maximum of skin-to-skin contact, if you are both naked.*

*Whatever you do to the back will be pleasurable, and the warmth created by the friction of hands and skin will certainly ease any aches and pains your partner has in this area. However, it is best to keep away from the actual spines of the backbone because these can be tender. Otherwise, be guided by the response of the receiver. Use deep probing movements with several fingertips bunched together to form a pad; walk your fingers deeply around the muscles; **far right**; use long sliding and gliding strokes with the flats of your hands; pinch areas of skin between finger and thumb; grip quite large areas of the top of the back between thumb and several fingers; **right**; and lastly, cover the back with tiny, feather-like touches as if a spider were walking over it. Never tickle your partner as this spoils the flow and the relaxation.*

As you learn, listen to what your partner says feels best and perhaps after their giving it a mark out of five, try to make things so good that by the end of the session you have increased the score to five. However experienced you are, always aim to produce the best possible sensations.

SMOOTHING THE ARMS

With your partner still lying face down, it is usually easy to progress to the arms. Start off by oiling the arms all over, one at a time, perhaps sitting astride or between your partner's open legs. Do some long strokes that slide down both arms at once, starting at the shoulders and ending at the fingertips; **below**. Go slowly. Beginners tend to do everything too fast.

Now turn your partner over, kneel at her side and run your hands down one arm from top to bottom, overlapping the paths of the hands in a wave-like motion as you come downwards. Most people receiving this find it wholly luxurious.

Now raise the arm so that the forearm is at right angles to the floor. Supporting the wrist with one hand, milk the muscles of the forearm with the other hand, pressing the side of your thumb firmly into the muscles; **below right**.

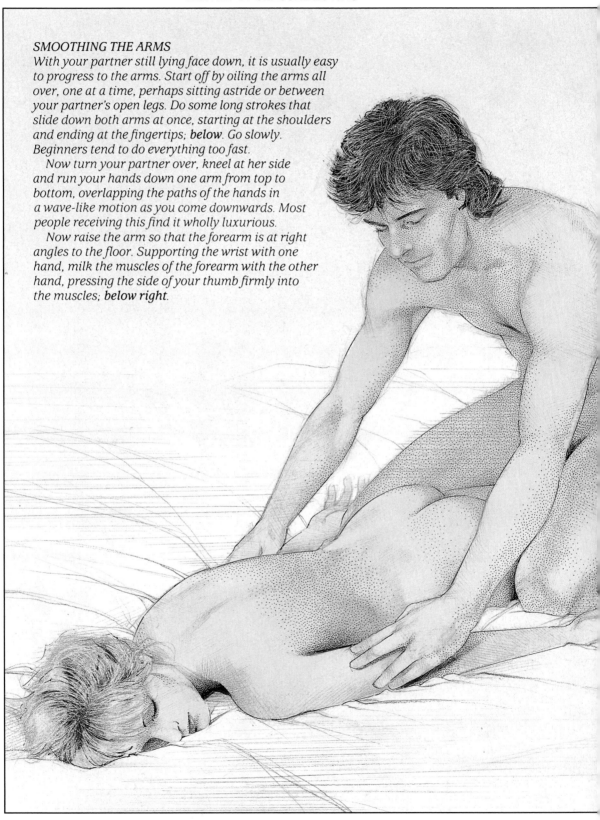

If you have time, you can now go to the top of your partner and, kneeling astride her, massage under her shoulders, with her lying on her back. Her body weight helps you knead her muscles at the top of her back, and this can lead to a sliding movement that travels down the arms. This combination of shoulder and arm massage can be quite delightful.

As with the massage of any part of the body, complete it by doing some long, slow, gliding, integrating strokes over the whole arm, and finish by trailing your fingertips off the tips of hers in a sensual way.

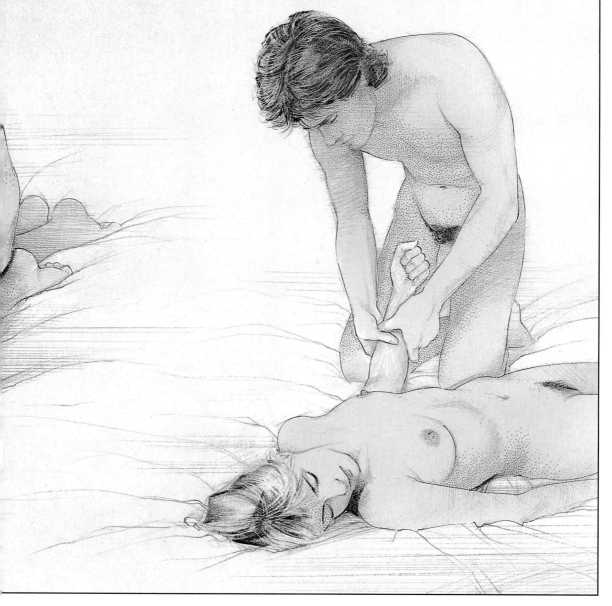

HOLDING HANDS
Hands are extremely sensitive and rewarding areas to massage. Many people experience tension in their hands, as is demonstrated by fiddling with things, tapping fingers, drumming out rhythms, and so on. As with the feet, the hands have reflex connections with all parts of the body and in the brain, disproportionately large areas are devoted to them, when you consider their size.

*Start by asking your partner to rest his hand, palm up, on the floor. Holding it by the wrist, firmly but gently, massage the palm; **below**. Try to find the area that feels best, as this differs greatly from person to person. Keep exploring the palm for some time, until you can produce blissful sensations. Now, gently pull the fingers one at time, but be cautious because many people are apprehensive about this. Hold the hand firmly at the wrist as you do this; **right**.*

Now place your hand against that of your partner so that your fingers match up palm to palm. Gently slide your fingers between his and draw them up so as to massage the sides of the fingers.

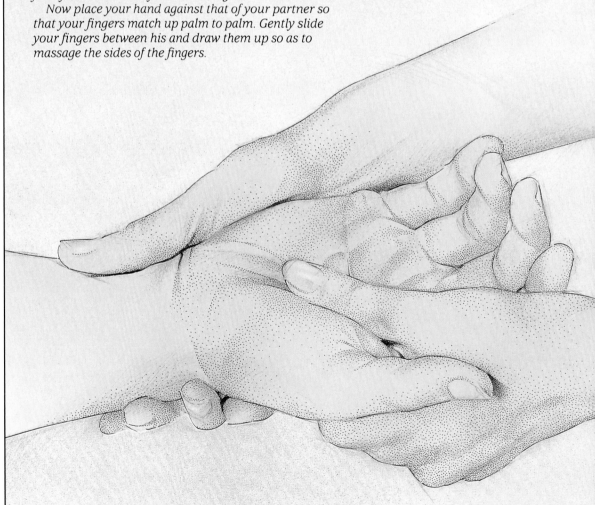

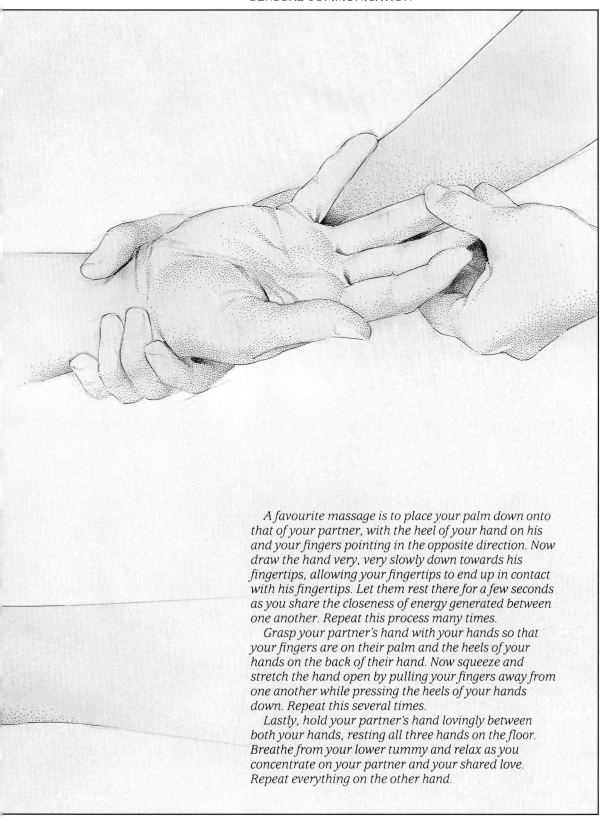

A favourite massage is to place your palm down onto that of your partner, with the heel of your hand on his and your fingers pointing in the opposite direction. Now draw the hand very, very slowly down towards his fingertips, allowing your fingertips to end up in contact with his fingertips. Let them rest there for a few seconds as you share the closeness of energy generated between one another. Repeat this process many times.

Grasp your partner's hand with your hands so that your fingers are on their palm and the heels of your hands on the back of their hand. Now squeeze and stretch the hand open by pulling your fingers away from one another while pressing the heels of your hands down. Repeat this several times.

Lastly, hold your partner's hand lovingly between both your hands, resting all three hands on the floor. Breathe from your lower tummy and relax as you concentrate on your partner and your shared love. Repeat everything on the other hand.

THIGHS, CALVES, FEET AND TOES

Start with the fronts of the legs with your partner on his back. Kneel astride the leg that you are to massage so that his foot is between your knees. Having oiled the leg, lean forward and run your hands down from the groin in a long, slow, gliding movement with one hand on either side of the leg. Meet at the foot and leave the foot gently via the toes. Repeat this flow with each leg several times.

Continue working the same areas, but this time with overlapping hand paths in an alternating hand, wave-like motion as you come down the leg to the foot. Repeat this several times, on both legs.

Next, move your whole body up the leg a little so that you are kneeling about level with his knees. Using both thumbs, press firmly into the muscles of the thigh with the thumbs across the upper leg and parallel to one another. This forms a sort of bar that you push quite firmly up the leg to the groin. Repeat this several times on both upper legs. This type of massage is not advisable on the lower leg because the shin bone is close to the surface and the procedure causes pain.

Before turning your partner over, go to the feet and, grasping both ankles, lean back and pull firmly for some time. This stretches the lower back and can feel quite exquisite. Relax for a few seconds and repeat. Some, women especially, like the insides of their thighs massaged, as there is a tunnel between the muscles there. Start at the inside of the knee and run your hand up to the groin, but do not touch the genitals.

*Now turn your partner over and oil the back of the legs. Put his foot flat onto your chest, and using your thumbs in parallel with one another as a bar, milk the calf muscles as you did those in the thigh; **right**. Repeat this in several waves from ankle to knee.*

Kneel between his thighs and massage the back of them, including perhaps his buttocks.

*Now to the feet. Many people fear that their feet will be ticklish, but if you go about the massage confidently and use big hand movements and holds, you should have no problem. Hold the foot first for a few seconds between both your palms. Now, sitting well away from the foot to be massaged, pull it from the forefoot ensuring that one hand is always in contact so that the foot cannot fall to the ground; **far right**. Do this for some minutes if you can.*

Next, put the foot gently on the floor and with one hand underneath, use the thumb of the other to massage all over the sole. Find the best places and massage them until your partner is satisfied.

Lastly, pull the toes gently and run your fingers between them.

ABDOMINAL AREAS

The stomach can be a ticklish area, so work cautiously until your partner becomes confident. Kneel either at her side, between her open legs, or over her thighs with her legs together; **right***, whichever you find best. Oil the area thoroughly and then run flat hands around the tummy area, starting with one hand at twelve o'clock and the other at six. Always go clockwise or it can be unpleasant. Move both hands at once around the tummy overlapping your hands at a quarter to three, to complete the circle. Do this circuit several times if it is pleasant.*

This can be followed by repeating the process, but now using small circular movements of the hands as the hands themselves move in circles. Mimic the twisting ride at the fairground as the hands rotate as they move clockwise.

A pleasant follow-on from this is to trace a path with both hands from the right groin, and without turning your partner over, to the small of the back on that side, up to the area at the bottom of the breastbone; under the left ribcage, back to the left small of the back and down to the left groin. This tracks a large diamond shape and, if done slowly, is very relaxing.

Now kneel at your partner's side. Oil all along one of her sides from chest to thigh. Reach over her body and pull the skin upwards on one side only from very near the floor so that your hands come to the front alternately. Move the hands downwards towards her hips overlapping the tracks as you do so, ensuring that one hand is in contact with her side at any one time. When you get to just below the hip, repeat again from the chest. Pull the hands nearly to the midline each time and be sure to start the pulling well back near the floor. Repeat on the other side of the body. The sensation this produces is fantastic.

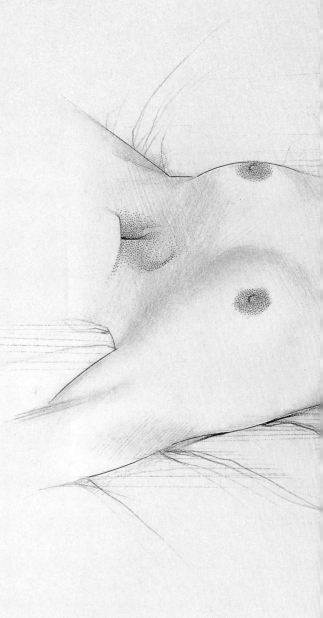

FACIAL REFRESHMENT

*The face does not need oiling; you will have plenty on
your hands by now. Kneel at the head and gently rest
your hands on your partner's face so that the palms
cover most of it and shut out the light; **right**. This is a
good, relaxing, starting and finishing position. Now,
keeping your fingertips fixed at the temple areas, start
running your thumbs firmly over the skin at the midline
above the nose, towards the ears. Do this same
movement over the eyebrows; **below**. Next, move down
and repeat the same sort of massage on the cheekbones,
but very gently.*

*Massage the muscles in front of the ears and lastly
run your bunched fingers firmly under the jaw on both
sides at once. Finish by covering the face once more, and
holding your hands there for some minutes.*

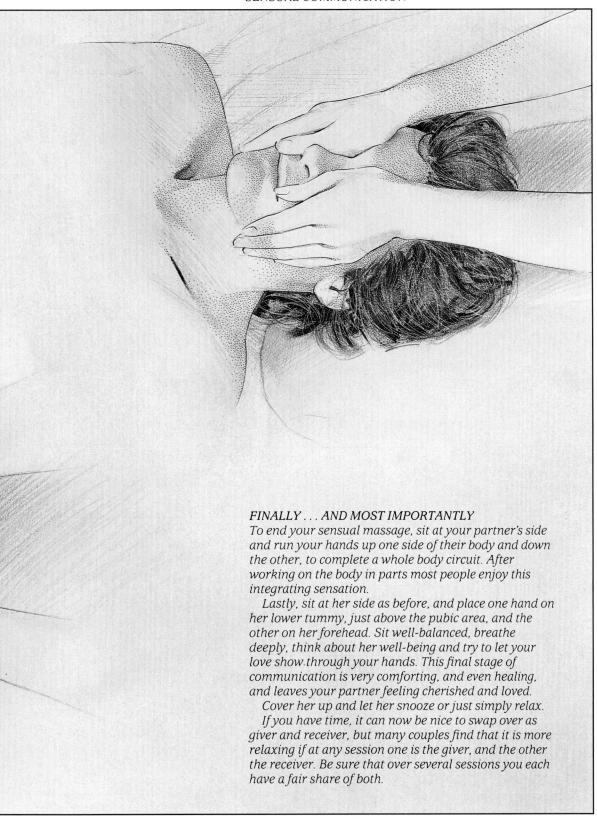

FINALLY . . . AND MOST IMPORTANTLY

To end your sensual massage, sit at your partner's side
and run your hands up one side of their body and down
the other, to complete a whole body circuit. After
working on the body in parts most people enjoy this
integrating sensation.

Lastly, sit at her side as before, and place one hand on
her lower tummy, just above the pubic area, and the
other on her forehead. Sit well-balanced, breathe
deeply, think about her well-being and try to let your
love show through your hands. This final stage of
communication is very comforting, and even healing,
and leaves your partner feeling cherished and loved.

Cover her up and let her snooze or just simply relax.

If you have time, it can now be nice to swap over as
giver and receiver, but many couples find that it is more
relaxing if at any session one is the giver, and the other
the receiver. Be sure that over several sessions you each
have a fair share of both.

KISSING AND CUDDLING

Most couples like to kiss and cuddle at some stage in their lovemaking. These agreeable pastimes take us back to infancy with its feelings of security, love and physical comfort. Sadly, many couples forget about the tenderness and excitement of kissing and cuddling, yet these activities are fundamental to any close, loving relationship.

When a couple who share loving feelings for one another want to demonstrate their affection, one of the first things they do is to kiss and cuddle. Most of us start with the head, neck and face because these are easily accessible parts. These are also areas we are used to having touched when we are babies and young children. For lovers who are discovering more about one another they represent areas of the body that are fairly safe and non-threatening both to the giver and the receiver. After all, a kiss on the cheek or head is socially acceptable in many settings, and does not necessarily serve as a prelude to intercourse.

When starting to express affection, most of us are fairly cautious, to reduce the chances of rejection. Starting with the head area increases the likelihood of the expressions of love being taken further. Kissing your lover's face, perhaps while holding it tenderly, is a good way to begin. Kiss it all over, including the eyes, eyebrows, under the chin, the tip of the nose, and so on. Many people relish having their ears kissed, but some find it unbearably ticklish, so beware!

Leave kissing the mouth until you feel that your partner is relaxed and happy. Plant tiny kisses on the mouth at first, rather than going for deep, exploratory embraces with your tongue. Try to gently tease with your lips, so as to increase the anticipation. Kiss your partner's mouth a little, then kiss somewhere else on their head or face. Perhaps nuzzle softly into their hair. From discussions I have had with my patients, it appears that there are as many kissing techniques and preferences as there are individuals. On balance, most people tell me that they prefer drier, firmer kisses to wetter, sloppier ones, but even this is an over-generalization. However you like to kiss it is courteous to ensure that your mouth is fresh and pleasant. Keep your teeth clean, visit your dentist regularly, and if you have bad breath it could be something that you have eaten. Try brushing your tongue with a toothbrush. Research in the United States shows that this technique, combined with toothbrushing, cures most cases of bad breath. If you smoke, be aware that a non-smoker may find it distasteful and avoid smoking for some time before kissing.

When you both want to become more adventurous, you might practise different kinds of kissing. Try running your tongue around the inside of your

---

By licking and bathing her with his tongue he can bring her to a high state of arousal without even touching her genitals.

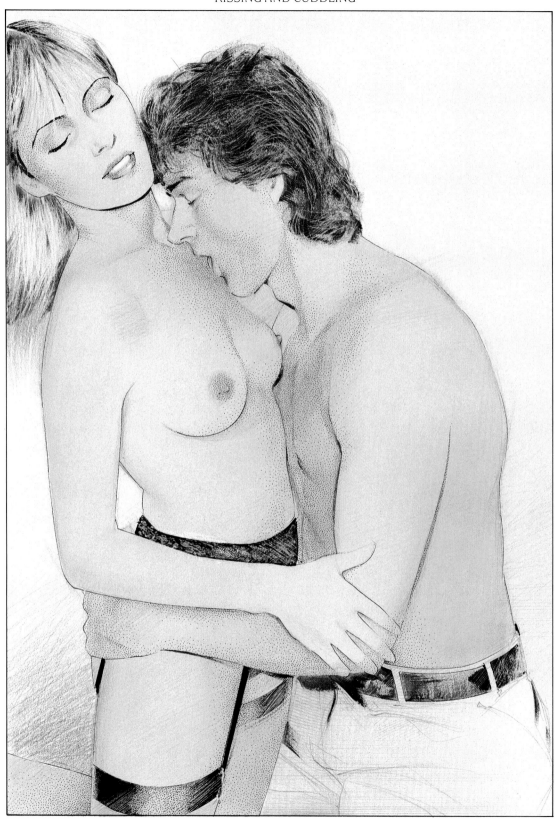

partner's lips. Perhaps massage her tongue with your tongue and then probe deeply under her tongue. Sucking one another's tongues can be delightful too. Experiment until you find what satisfies and pleases you both best.

Kissing each other intimately will naturally bring your bodies close together. Use your hands to touch and caress as much as you feel will be welcome, according to the level of intimacy that you share. Hugging one another close feels very comforting, an embrace need not be passionate, and just holding one another firmly can be highly pleasurable even if you do nothing else.

As you progress, either in a new relationship, or along well-trodden paths in an existing one, you will now find that you are becoming quite pleasantly aroused, and will want to involve more of your partner's body. Cuddling with clothes on can be highly erotic, even for experienced lovers, and slipping a seductive hand under clothes can be even more exciting for either partner.

As you progress, be sure to respond to your partner, to reassure them that you are happy with what is happening. You do not have to talk – sighs, little moans, slight body movements to accommodate a new caress, all convey more than words. Train yourself to be alert for these tell-tale signs.

Most women are more stimulated by all-over body caressing than are men. However, there are many more pleasurable areas for the average man than he realizes. Exciting places that often get overlooked by lovers caressing their partners are behind the knees, the insides of the thighs, the shoulders, the ear lobes, the fingers, and the bottom.

As you stroke and caress one another you will probably find that you want to say intimate, provocative things to increase the level of excitement, and also to express your love and affection. Aural sex is very powerful and few of us are immune to personal flattery or tempting suggestions. Partners can tend to be somewhat sparing on praise of each other, either because of familiarity or shyness, but here is an ideal opportunity to share personal, intimate feelings about one another. As you relax into each other's arms, becoming as one with your lover, you will probably feel uninhibited and relaxed, able to open up about all manner of things, that often have no direct relevance to the matter in hand. Some people cry, with pleasure or pain; others share a problem that has been bothering them; some say something personal about their partner's value, that would be impossible to say face-to-face over breakfast; and so on. This caring openness should be at the heart of all good lovemaking and indeed forms the basis for true, sharing intercourse.

Whatever you do and however you do it, be sure you are interpreting your partner's body language, receiving and acting on their responses, and maintaining a flowing rapport. Visible or audible signs of your pleasure will excite your partner, perhaps stimulating them to enhance the enjoyment. As you both experiment, remember to be considerate lovers. Too violent a 'lovebite' will leave a mark that could embarrass. Never inflict any pain unless you know exactly what your partner enjoys. Gentle nibbling and biting can be highly arousing but taken too far are a nuisance and even unpleasant. Be attuned to your partner's body, caressing and cuddling while you are kissing.

By now you will probably both be starting to become pleasantly aroused and will want to progress to more erotic pursuits.

EROTIC MASSAGE

*Here we discuss the erotic bridge between sensual massage and
true intercourse. Many couples move straight from playful
cuddling, hugging and kissing to intercourse, but they could be
missing out on more excitement, as we shall see. For the couple
who do not, for some reason, want to have actual intercourse,
erotic massage can turn into an exhilarating adventure
which ends in masturbation.*

Whether or not you have reached this stage of lovemaking via sensual
massage, you can now have hours of fun exploring the temptations of
true erotic massage. The difference here is that the aim is to tease and arouse
one another, perhaps as a prelude to intercourse. This represents the beginning
of a pleasuring that most people call foreplay. Of course, pleasuring such as
this is every bit as much lovemaking as is penetrative sex, yet many couples
cut it short or treat it as a hurdle that must be overcome before they indulge in
'the real thing'.

If you and your partner are to achieve the best possible pleasure through
erotic massage, you will both need to be aware of each other's most sensuous
spots. The whole body is covered with nerve endings that feed information
back to the brain, but certain areas are more richly endowed. In both sexes, the
fingers, toes and lips are especially sensitive and can be highly erotic if sucked
or gently stroked. The nipples too, are the centre of wonderful sensations for
many people, much to the surprise of some men. The genital area is the
obvious place to produce erotic stimulation, but many couples concentrate on
this area too soon, and ignore the marvellous potential of the rest of their
bodies.

Although sensual massage is undoubtedly best done on the floor, most
couples find that this setting is rather unromantic for erotic massage. Get
undressed and go to bed, then try to think creatively about how you might use
your body to 'massage' your partner. You can use your hands, of course, but
what about using other parts too, such as your hair, the rest of your body, or
sensual and erotic materials.

When using your hands, employ long, luxurious strokes to produce the most
arousing effects. Position your body in such a way as to stimulate your
partner's in the most exciting way. Sit astride, for example, so that your pubic
area is in contact with your partner's skin. Run your hands slowly over the
special places, and your partner will respond with expressions of pleasure.
These gliding movements can be extended and varied by including some
kneading. This works especially well on the buttocks. Take large handfuls of
flesh and squeeze fairly firmly. Try alternating this with really light, featherlike
touches with your fingertips, but be sure not to tickle.

Smacking can be both stimulating and fun. Put your partner over your knee
and gently but firmly, smack their bottom. Many people, and women

especially, say that this is highly arousing. Perhaps follow this by kissing the areas you have just smacked. Then softly massage your partner with your hair, if it is long enough. Run your hair all over the body and especially the genitals.

You should both be starting to tingle all over. How about massaging one another with some sensual or erotic materials? Silk, fur, rubber, feathers, or anything else that you have to hand can be arousing in quite surprising ways. Some lovers massage one another with creamy foods. For example, he might massage her breasts with yoghurt or cream and then slowly lick it off. 'Warm' ice that has been out of the freezer for some time can produce delicious sensations. Try putting some in your mouth and then sucking parts of your partner's body. The effect can be exquisite.

Think about using the rest of your body to massage your partner. As a woman, you can rub him with your breasts and nipples, and if he takes the time, he can excite you with sensitive breast massage. Then, run the inside of your thigh all over his body including his erect nipples. This will be erotic for you both. Massage him with your feet, the inside of your arm, your back, and so on. Experiment with your bodies to see what feels good for you both.

As the sexual temperature rises, you will probably extend your normal kissing to include tongue massaging. Obviously you will want to kiss and excite your partner's erogenous zones, but you can use your mouth even more creatively. Run it softly over these sensitive areas and you will produce electric effects; wet an area and then blow gently over it; nibble the skin and cover it with tiny bites; suck intimate places into your mouth and work your tongue on them. How about giving your partner a tongue bath? Using your tongue, bathe your partner all over, as if you were washing them. A natural extension of this for many couples is to kiss very erotically areas such as the palms of the hands, the fingertips, and the toes. Take the fingers into your mouth one at a time, watching your partner's reaction. Oral sex has become far too narrow a pursuit for many couples, confined as it generally is, to the genitals. The whole of your partner's body can be highly erotic, and will tremble with pleasure if you use your mouth ingeniously.

Some couples like to use an electric massager. These are available from chemist shops and drugstores, and usually plug into the mains. The best ones fit onto the hand so that they vibrate as the hand massages the receiver's body. Other types of massager or vibrator are considered on page 127.

Exactly what you do, and how you do it, will come with practice and has to be tailor-made to suit your partner. Never make the mistake of thinking that because you have discovered what best suits one lover that the same things will necessarily apply to another. Of course, we all call upon our previous experience in such matters but this should be done sensibly, and with caution.

Finally, I would like to discuss some very specific erotic massage techniques that lead directly on to mutual masturbation. Both men and women can enjoy being more adventurous when massaging their partners' genital areas. When

He has already kissed her all over with his mouth and is now starting to involve her genitals.

massaging a man it is, of course, nice to concentrate on the penis, but also remember to massage its root (towards the man's bottom) and the area between the anus and the base of the penis. Many men also like to have their anal area massaged, perhaps along with fondling the buttocks.

Squeeze his testicles gently but firmly with your hands, and even probe his scrotum deeply with your tongue. Take a testicle into your mouth and massage it with your tongue. Massage his groin area, and then turn him over onto his tummy. At either side of the crack at the top of his bottom there are areas that, if stimulated well, can be highly erotic. Put one fingertip of each hand on these points and make small, circular vibratory movements. Trial and error will enable you to find the magic spot. Keep up this massage for some minutes and be aware of his response.

When massaging a woman, first put her on her tummy and knead and stroke her bottom for some time. Most women find this exciting and arousing in itself. Let a finger run in between her buttocks, and even caress her anus if she likes it. Now slip your fingers further down so that you can massage the area between her vagina and her anus. Do the vibratory massage at either side of the lower spine as described for the man, above.

Now turn her over and gently massage her whole vulval area, perhaps after oiling it well with a bland massage oil. Massage her groin if you know she likes this, and then turn your attention to her vulva. Run your fingers up and down her outer lips, holding them gently between finger and thumb. Next, grasp one of the outer lips between finger and thumb and gently pull it outwards. Let it go. Work from top to bottom on one lip, gently pulling and letting go and then repeat the process on the other side. Many women tell me that this feels exquisite. End up by stroking and teasing the opening to the vagina, especially at its bottom.

For some couples, the ultimate pleasure of erotic massage is internal massage. If you are massaging a woman, try firmly stroking into the mouth of the vagina with your fingers at the eight o'clock or half-past five positions. (The clitoris is at twelve o'clock.) Both of these are favourites, but always make sure you are doing what your partner likes best. This will usually involve ensuring that she is very wet before attempting any sort of internal massage. If you have aroused her well she will be lubricating herself but if she is not, either spend more time or use a lubricating jelly or even massage oil. Further explorations and internal massage are discussed on page 123.

Some men like their anus penetrated and find their prostrate gland highly erotic when massaged by their lover. We see how to stimulate the male 'G spot' on page 139.

From this, albeit brief, description, you should be becoming aware that any adventurous couple can create a whole new erotic life for themselves, given a little thought and time. Many of us are too timid, too wary, and too rushed in our lovemaking to explore the tremendous variety of pleasures that could be possible. Is it any surprise then that so many complain that their lovemaking is boring, and that they have every 'right' to look for another partner? My clinical experience suggests that the best possible rewards are available at home for most loving couples, if only they set aside the time and effort to develop them.

MASTURBATION: A PLEASURE TO BE SHARED

Although most of us learn to masturbate very early in life, this is usually a rehearsal for what is to come later. Lessons learned even as early as infancy, about what we find exciting and pleasurable, live with us for a whole lifetime and shape our sexual lives with our partners.

Most of use learn to masturbate in the cradle or during very early childhood At this age we alight on our genitals by chance, find that they feel good to touch and play with, and go on to produce various sensations that seem pleasurable at the time. Some children, and especially girls, never stop masturbating from now on. In fact, about one third of all women say that they cannot remember a time when they did not masturbate, right from early childhood. Those that do stop, start again at around puberty, when both sexes develop masturbation techniques that remain with them for life.

Although much has been said about masturbation in the past, in a book such as this, dedicated as it is to enriching a couple's sex life together, we shall only consider masturbation in the context of a loving one-to-one relationship.

Of course, for some people, the two do not go together. They imagine, quite wrongly, that once they have a solid, loving relationship, masturbation should be abandoned. This is not so. The vast majority of even very happily married men and women masturbate from time to time, if only when their partner is unavailable sexually. Masturbation provides excitement and a quality of orgasm that is different from that enjoyed with a partner during intercourse. And who would deny any individual a source of sexual pleasure that is not harmful, and can even enrich their sex life with their partner?

Few couples can truly claim that they have everything they want or sexually desire, within their relationship. Fantasy, coupled with masturbation, can easily make up for this deficit. Practised alone, masturbation need not be the lonely, solitary pastime that so many people make it out to be. After all, it is possible to be alone and not be lonely. Just because partners are committed to one another does not mean that their individual sexuality must die – nor should it be eclipsed by their partner.

Masturbation is usually an integral part of most one-to-one relationships, however otherwise fulfilling they are. The healthy, well-balanced couple realize this, and is not threatened by one partner masturbating, provided, of course, that it does not replace shared sexual activity.

But masturbation should not be just a solitary pursuit. In responsible, loving relationships, it is something that can be enjoyed either as a spectator or as a participant. Watching your partner is highly instructive and this is something that I recommend to all couples experiencing any sexual or relationship problems. Many individuals enjoy watching their partner masturbate. In particular, many men tell me that they find this arousing. By learning to observe in minute detail exactly what you do as you masturbate, your partner can discover much about your arousal cycle that can be of use to improve intercourse and to stimulate or masturbate you exactly how you would best like. Such lessons cannot be learned from books – they are highly personal to you.

Particular points you should notice about your partner's masturbation include body position; what is done to parts of the body other than the genitals; what breathing changes occur, facial expression, body position and so on, as climax approaches; how the genitals are stimulated, including the speed, length of stroke, pressure and so on; the signs of imminent orgasm; and what exactly happens at orgasm (how far he spurts his semen, how many such

They are relaxed together, and he is communicating his pleasure to her. She encloses his penis firmly with her fingers, in just the way he does when masturbating himself; she is stimulating his nipples for added eroticism; her naked body against his excites him further, while her sexy attire feeds his fantasies.

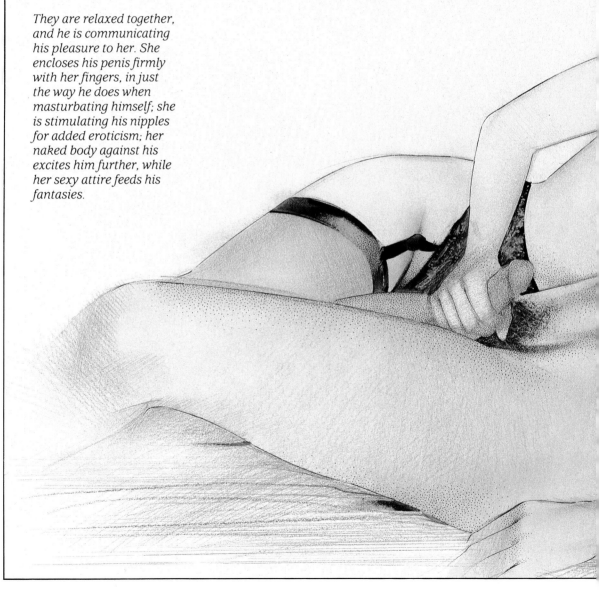

spurts there are, and so on). Obviously a man should also be able to detail his partner's progress to climax in exactly the same way.

Lessons learned here are a valuable investment for the average couple because not only do such exercises enable each person to feel more at ease with the other, but they also leave little to the imagination – which can play such unfortunate tricks on the best of us if we are ignorant.

The next step from this sort of exercise is to learn how to stimulate your partner in a way that gives them at least as much pleasure as when they stimulate themselves. Practice makes perfect, and it takes a lot of practice if you are to come anywhere near being able to replicate your partner's own unique methods of masturbation. This is a real challenge and once perfected,

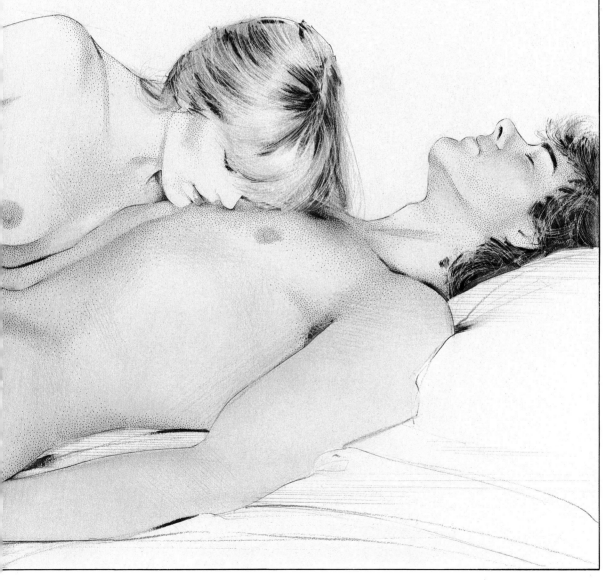

This is an exceptionally good position for mutual masturbation. There is lots of body contact; both can easily reach one another's genital area; and he can kiss her and nuzzle into her hair whilst caressing her breasts with his hands. She has a hand free to guide his towards what she best likes, and can reach round to stimulate his body where he most wants.

will be of great value in your sexual life together. It is my experience that, in far too many cases, a couple strive to make things happen, but often one partner is unaware of what the other likes, and neither can communicate this without fear of rejection, loss or ridicule.

There are several things worth bearing in mind when learning to masturbate one another. They are worth remembering because so many couples try to give and receive pleasure in this way yet fail to achieve it because of quite simple things which could, with a little planning, have been prevented. For instance, getting the position right is essential when masturbating someone. As the receiver, you must be as comfortable as the giver. The best positions involve getting your genitals as near those of your partner as possible.

Setting the scene and getting the mood right helps a lot too. Dimmed lights, a little alcohol, some favourite music, sexy literature or a raunchy video can all contribute to the atmosphere. Keep the lights on so that you can watch your partner's expressions. This in itself can be highly arousing.

Use plenty of lubrication on either the penis or the clitoris. Be aware that dryness is the enemy of good masturbation. KY jelly is ideal but a bland massage oil will do. A man can be masturbated using talc but this is not suitable for a woman.

It is also essential in the early days to talk to one another often. Few couples are telepathic, and most need quite specific instructions, even after watching the other on several occasions. Part of this communication should also include saying what you like done to other parts of your body.

Many women say that they prefer to have exactly the same things done, time and time again, when they are masturbated. It is the very predictability of the pleasure that they enjoy. Some men say the same, but many encourage more variation than the average woman.

Once you have discussed, practiced and mastered all of this, you will be able to masturbate one another individually or mutually, whenever you might want to. Many women are reluctant to have sex after a baby; others do not want sex during a period, or even premenstrually; there will be times when it will be impossible to have sex, for example, after a gynaecological operation or if either of you have a genital infection; and so on. More often than any of these specific times, are those occasions when one of you wants sex but the other does not feel like it for some reason. Partners whose sexual repertoire contains wonderful masturbation will never be left feeling resentful or unfulfilled, and they can rely on the other to answer their sexual needs when intercourse is not a possibility.

For the couple who are unsure of one another's sexual health or fidelity, erotic massage followed by masturbation or mutual masturbation is a fulfilling and exciting alternative to intercourse. For the steady couple who are faithful to each other and have a rich and fulfilling sex life, masturbation can complement their lovemaking skills and will always be a welcome standby or a pleasant change.

ORAL LOVEMAKING

Using your mouth to stimulate your lover's body is a natural part of lovemaking. Most couples like kissing, and not just on the lips, and the majority also enjoy having their body licked and sucked in various creative ways. Unfortunately, the term 'oral sex' has become restrictive, suggesting that lovers only stimulate one another's genitals orally. This need not be so.

From our earliest days in babyhood, we learn that the mouth is an exceptionally sensitive and rewarding area of our body. In the first few weeks of life we suck from our mother's breast or from a bottle, and there is little doubt that these pleasurable memories remain with us, however unconsciously, right into adulthood.

The mouth then, is our first erotic zone. This might come as a surprise to some readers, but few who have watched a very young baby feeding at the breast will deny that there is a great deal more going on than the delivery of nutrients. The baby comes to enjoy the closeness of mother's body, her comforting heartbeat, her warmth, the love she shows, and perhaps even her smiles, songs or loving talk.

All of this makes a lasting impression on a baby, and it appears that a child that has plenty of such loving experiences goes on to eat well, not to suck its thumb, will probably never use a dummy or pacifier, and will be less likely to smoke as an adult. In other words, his needs for oral gratification will have been largely met by a loving mother who feeds her baby when it wants and uses her nipple or a bottle as a comforter, and not just as a source of nutrients.

However well we are looked after as infants most of us retain a pleasant memory and want to repeat the joys of the oral stage of our psychosexual and erotic development. When I say 'erotic', I do not necessarily mean that genital activity or excitement is involved. Sometimes, of course, it is, as any experienced breastfeeding mother can tell. Many women notice that during a particularly close, rewarding feed at the breast, a baby boy will obtain an erection. Clearly the equivalent response occurs with baby girls also, but is simply less obvious.

This suggests that the mouth becomes one of the most important erogenous zones. In fact, the sensory area of the brain that receives input from the lips and mouth is enormous, compared with that of almost any other area of the body.

Oral sex then, is simply any sexually stimulating and arousing activity produced by using the mouth. Kissing is the simplest and most obvious type of oral sex and, as we have already seen, the mouth can be used in many creative ways to produce and receive erotic sensations with your partner. For most people though, true oral sex involves the genitals. This is still something of a taboo for many couples because the genitals are 'private' and the thought of such intimate contact can be intimidating, even to quite sexually aware individuals. For many, women especially, oral contact with her genitals remains one of the most intimate things a man can do. Many of my female patients tell me that intercourse is easy by comparison. This situation comes about as a result of so many people, and girls particularly, being brought up to think of their genitals as dirty, smelly or otherwise unwholesome.

Clearly anyone who has such fears, however unconscious, will have trouble being able to relax enough to enjoy oral-genital contact. However, I find that once such an individual does relax they are amazed and delighted by the exquisite sensations they experience.

Oral sex is totally safe. There is only any danger if one or other of you has any kind of venereal disease or infection. Also, if you have a cold sore it makes sense not to suck or kiss one another's genitals. This is because the herpes virus in cold sores can be transferred to the genitals and cause infection there. If there is any doubt that you might be HIV-positive or if there is any hint of possible genital infection, I strongly recommend that you do not engage in oral sex until you have been cleared by a doctor.

Assuming that you are both free from genital infections and have no cold sores, the next thing to think about is genital cleanliness. Whilst oral sex is highly pleasurable to most people – indeed in many polls of sexual behaviour it has come 'top of the pops' – no one likes oral contact with genitals that are unclean. Both the vagina and a man's penis come to smell of their natural secretions if they are left unwashed for a day. Partners who indulge in oral sex should always ensure that their genitals are immaculately washed. This means bathing at least once a day or washing the genitals immediately before sex might occur. Bathing or showering together can be fun and washing one another's genitals can become a part of foreplay. Be careful when washing the vagina; there is never any need to wash inside. Use scented soaps and vaginal deodorants with caution because many women find that they irritate delicate skin. Warm water and plain, unscented soap usually suffices.

There are just a couple of points worth remembering before you begin. Firstly, agree some rules. For instance, a woman may be happy to take her man's penis into her mouth, but not into her throat, or to have him ejaculate in her mouth. Set out the rules in advance so that there is no unpleasantness at the last moment. Each partner should never go further than they both agree in advance. The man who thrusts deep into his partner's throat as he climaxes is not only inconsiderate but could do her great harm as she chokes on the unexpected penis. For this reason, many women say that they best enjoy sucking a man's penis if they can control the depth of penetration.

Never bite the sex organs, however gently or playfully. A man's penis that is bitten bleeds like fury. And never, ever blow into the genitals. This is possibly dangerous for a man but can be lethal for a woman, as air is forced into her uterus and up into her fallopian tubes.

Many women who indulge in oral sex regularly keep their pubic hair trimmed and some couples even make a sexy game of this, as the man trims it for her, depilates her, or shaves her, according to what they both like.

Now let us look at how a man can best arouse a woman through oral sex. First, it is vital to get into a comfortable position because when she is lying down her genitals are low and close to the bed, and stimulating them orally for any length of time can be hard on the man's neck. Perhaps raise her pelvis on a pillow or two, or kneel on the floor in front of her, between her legs, with her bottom right on the edge of the bed.

Before actually starting to kiss her genitals, spend some time caressing them with your hands. Indeed you should keep your hands caressing her body all the time. Nuzzle into her vulva and kiss the area around her groin. Run your tongue lightly all over the area to tease and arouse her in anticipation.

Now you could kiss the labia majora, or large lips, and take them into your mouth one at a time. Run your tongue down the inside face of each in turn, starting at the top near the clitoris, sliding down to near the vagina. Suck the small lips, the labia minora, gently and then maybe run your tongue and lips up and down them, as you did with the large lips.

Next, go to the vagina itself and run the tip of your tongue around the opening but do not yet go inside. Let your tongue stray to the part between her vagina and anus and lick all around it firmly. Nudge your tongue in and out of

He has learned what stimulates her best by watching her masturbate and now he is putting it into practice using his mouth.

her vagina now in a teasing way. She will probably arch her pelvis to meet your tongue if she is highly aroused.

Her clitoris will now be growing erect and firm. Gently lick and kiss all around it. When she is keen for you to kiss the actual organ itself, tongue the shaft and its tip very carefully and be guided by what she best enjoys. Some women cannot bear to have their clitoris stimulated directly by hand yet find it magical to feel a tongue. As she becomes increasingly aroused, you might insert a couple of fingers into her vagina. Some women tell me they like their vaginal opening to be stretched widely – indeed that this is their best source of arousal. Keep caressing her with your hands, one perhaps on her breast or nipple, and the other in her vagina. A few women prefer a vibrator to fingers in their vagina, and a dildo can be highly pleasurable too. (The use of these is described in the next section.) Experiment and talk with her, to find what is best. Keep the whole area wet with saliva; stop and start so as to tease her, and raise her level of anticipation; and always be guided by her wishes.

Let us now look at how a woman can arouse a man through oral sex.

When approaching the penis, be careful not to bend it too far downwards. Basically, the erect penis naturally points upwards, or thereabouts. Perhaps begin by simply kissing it. After all, oral sex can be regarded as an extension of other oral lovemaking, and this should come naturally once you gain experience. Smother the penis with kisses, being sure to keep your teeth out of the way. It is important to get yourself into a really comfortable position, so that you do not get neck-ache. As you kiss the penis more, try licking it like a lollipop. Run your tongue around the head in a swirling motion, and be sure to give plenty of attention to the little ridge on the underside where the head joins the shaft. This frenum, as it is called, is exquisitely sensitive for most men and can make some men come to a climax in seconds. If this is not what you want, be careful to be aware of how much you are stimulating it. Now try licking the shaft of the penis, applying the full width of your tongue, and running it down to his testicles. Then perhaps swirl your tongue around the scrotum, probing deeply into it. Gently take one testicle into your mouth and suck on it. Compress it with your mouth, but do not bite. Now, move up to the head of the penis again and, taking it into your mouth, use your tongue creatively to stimulate the tip.

Tease him by taking the penis out of your mouth and putting it on your palm, then suck it, kiss it tenderly, and do anything else that you know he likes. When he seems to be really excited, put it into your mouth again and suck it hard a few times. Next, push his penis in and out of your mouth as deeply as feels good for you and bring him to orgasm, if that is what you have both agreed. If either of you does not want to do this, then keep on stimulating him until he ejaculates, perhaps over your breasts, or into a paper hanky that you have handy. If you have agreed to take the semen into your mouth you can swallow it if you want to – it is perfectly safe, and you cannot, of course, get pregnant by doing this.

Always keep your hands moving over his body, perhaps stroking his genitals, anus, bottom, nipples, or whatever he best enjoys. Remember to take your time, to stop to tease him and to do exactly what he likes best, not just what you found worked for another man.

Partners that take this much time and trouble to pleasure one another orally find they have a very rewarding sex life. Indeed, for some couples, oral sex becomes a perfectly acceptable alternative to penis in vagina sex if this is not available for some reason, perhaps one partner has just had an operation or infection, or intercourse is particularly painful.

There are few couples who fail to find oral sex highly arousing even when they do not particularly feel like having intercourse. Many individuals find that they can be brought to a second or subsequent orgasm with oral caresses even if this would not be possible using any other method. This also works very well for the man who needs to be re-aroused soon after an orgasm.

In this position the woman can easily control depth of penetration with her hand, and he can caress her as she excites him.

*It is essential when using
any sort of sex toy to
personalize its use to the
individual with whom one
is making love.*

126

TIME FOR PLAY

*Sex toys have been favourites with lovers since recorded history.
As sexual pleasure enhancers, they can have dramatic effects
and also add an element of fun to any relationship. They open
up new ranges of experience for normally unadventurous lovers
and are of use to couples who are bored or possibly inhibited.
Sex toys are not kinky or weird, are easily obtainable through
mail order, and are not addictive!*

There are many types of sex aids or toys, the vast majority of which are aimed at couples who want to enrich their sex lives, and the biggest seller of them all is the simple penis-shaped vibrator. This plastic toy is designed for stimulating the vulva, nipples, clitoris, vagina, or anus. Some women like the sensations produced by vibrating on the outside of their body and others most enjoy those produced inside them, perhaps on the front vaginal wall, where their G-spot is located. Men can also gain pleasure from the sensations of a vibrator, but far fewer men than women say that it is a favourite toy.

Vibrators are battery-powered or plug into the mains. If you buy a battery-powered one, make sure the batteries are always fresh. Lack of power is clearly not a problem with the mains-powered varieties but some women are wary of mains electricity being used near their genitals. There is no cause for concern.

The best place to use a vibrator on a man is at the tip of his penis over the frenum (see page 124). Press deeply into the penis and see the effect it has. Some men can climax with just this stimulation alone.

When using your vibrator, the only caution I would stress is that, as with any other sex toy that may enter your body, you must be scrupulous about keeping it clean. In particular, a vibrator that has been in or near an anus should be washed before placing it inside a vagina. And, whilst I am issuing cautions, you must, of course, be very careful not to share your sex toys with anyone else unless you are quite sure that the other person is clear of venereal infections. There is no danger to be had by using a vibrator in the anus provided that you always leave enough of it to hold onto firmly. If you put it in too far it can get lost.

The next most popular sex toy is the dildo or artificial penis. Dildos are usually made in firm latex and come in many sizes. If, as a woman, you are selecting one for yourself, you will probably choose one that is too small because you may easily under-estimate the diameter of your aroused vagina. A man, however, tends to buy a dildo for his partner that is too large. I recommend that choosing be done together and that you select a size up from that which the woman feels will be comfortable. Such a dildo will give maximum stimulation even when the vagina is widely open when aroused.

You can use a dildo in many different ways. Some women like to use one when they masturbate either alone or with their partner and others enjoy one being used in their vagina by their man as they become aroused during pleasuring. As a man, you will probably find that masturbating your partner and using a dildo at the same time is highly arousing for you, and it will leave the woman's hands free to caress her own body, particularly her breasts.

What women actually enjoy most with a dildo varies a lot. For some, inserting it deeply and holding it there is best, whereas others are unhappy unless it is being thrust in and out like a large penis. A few like it inserted very obliquely so that it stretches the vaginal opening yet penetrates very little.

Many more men enjoy anal stimulation than is generally realized – indeed both sexes often find anal stimulation an unexpected pleasure. There are small dildos made especially for anal use and special vibrators are popular too. Large latex butt plugs stretch the anal opening widely and are a favourite with some people of both sexes. I mentioned above the precautions necessary with any form of anal toy but apart from this there should be no cause for concern as no form of anal play produces AIDS of itself. It is only possible to catch AIDS by indulging in sex play with someone who has AIDS or is HIV-positive.

Many couples use a sexual lubricant of some kind during their sex lives. The best, safest and most widely available is KY jelly, a bland, water soluble sterile jelly that, apart from its coldness when used straight from the tube, is a pleasant, useful aid for almost any lover. Other varieties are available that have a more natural feel to them. One, made by a large reputable company, mimics vaginal secretions fairly accurately.

Lubricants are used if the woman is insufficiently aroused to make penetration easy; and on sex toys that are to be inserted into the vagina, and especially the anus. Dildos really need lubricating every time because the latex has no innate slippery qualities. If a dildo or vibrator is being used on a woman with a physical disability, lubrication is usually vital as normal vaginal secretions can be poor.

You can also have fun with condoms. They are mainly used as protectives against AIDS, other venereal diseases and unwanted pregnancy of course, and their use is discussed fully in the next chapter, but they can also be used as 'toys' by the couple who regularly use them. You can put a ribbed or contoured condom onto a vibrator, for example, or use one on the penis, for a different vaginal sensation. Most women say that condoms with unusual designs produce very small differences in sensation, but the fun element and novelty value of their use can sometimes enhance an otherwise routine love life, so give them a try.

Now I turn to the category of sex toys that are worth mentioning because with sensible use they can be a lot of fun, but which essentially are quite frivolous and without proven value. Many men think that their penises are too small and so there is clearly a market for 'penis enlargers'. The very simplest are rings that are worn around the base of the penis. They constrict the organ and prevent blood from leaving it. This produces a big, hard erection in most men. It is essential to use only professionally made rings because anything that is rigid and cannot be instantly released can be seriously hazardous.

Another way of 'enlarging' the penis is to wear a condom-like sheath that adds an inch or two to the length of the organ. This is strapped onto the penis and can help to give a man confidence, but this may be at the expense of reduced sensitivity for the woman, and indeed for the wearer. Most women are not much concerned about the length of their man's penis, unless it is terribly short, but if an artificial extension improves the man's ego and the woman is not inconvenienced, who is to say that it is a waste of time? However, creams, sprays, specialist lubricants and potions that claim extraordinarily increased sexual performance are all a complete waste of time and money.

Sexy underwear for both sexes is, after vibrators, the biggest selling group of products in the sex shop industry, and its use can certainly enliven a couple's loveplay sessions. It varies from skimpy and inventive garments designed to facilitate petting and making love, to high-quality lingerie that is more easily available from reputable department or specialist stores.

For the more adventurous, sex shops also sell toys and equipment that cater to the sado-masochistic market. We take a brief look at this subject on page 53. Suffice it to say, that increasing numbers of couples find that some sort of loveplay involving restraint, teasing, and even some pain, greatly enhances their arousal and quality of orgasm. The vast majority of these couples do not consider themselves to be 'kinky' and do not see what they do as at all unloving. It is simply that they have, for quite unconscious reasons, a need to give and receive 'pain' even though generally, the pain is somewhat symbolic. Simple pleasures in this area can be accommodated by tying one another up with any useful item that comes to hand for example, but for the creative and adventurous, special sex toys are available.

Books, magazines and videos are also highly popular sex aids. Few couples have never bought a sexy magazine and there is evidence that 'porn' videos are mostly bought or hired by perfectly conventional husbands and wives. In fact, this is a big growth market in all western countries.

Lastly, I would like to mention the purely fun items that have no real sexual purpose but give the receiver a giggle and perhaps a few moments of sexual delight. Phallic candles, arousing zodiac charts, naughty playing cards and so on, are old favourites, and have been for decades.

Sex toys are, and always have been, popular with creative lovers who want to enrich and enhance their sex lives. They reduce boredom; make us laugh; create new sensations that are unavailable to those who go for 'straight' sex only; are useful for the elderly and the disabled; and are usually well worth their cost. For the couple unsure of each other's sexual health, they can provide a rich and stimulating sex life when direct genital activity is unwise.

PRECAUTIONS AND PROTECTIVES

*Each time we indulge in sensual lovemaking to orgasm, or have
intercourse, we run the risk, however theoretical, that a child
will be conceived. The vast majority of sensual and intercourse
experiences though do not produce a baby, as sex has become
largely recreational rather than procreational. This section
serves to introduce the subject of safer sex and birth control.*

Most modern couples would blanch at the thought of their great-grandparent's sexual lives. A century ago a woman was probably plagued by the thought of unwanted pregnancy after unwanted pregnancy. They sapped her health, provided her with more mouths to feed and individuals to nurture, and undoubtedly affected her sexual relationship with her husband.

With the advent of modern contraception, the situation has changed dramatically and unwanted pregnancies, though still common, are much less of a hazard in one-to-one relationships. Women now have the freedom to choose whether, and when, they will become pregnant, and this has changed the face of human sexuality both in, and out, of the bedroom.

Traditionally, contraception has been a man's affair. The most popular method until the combined contraceptive Pill came into use in the late 1960s, was the condom, or sheath. Overall, male methods still predominate across the world today, if we exclude breastfeeding which is still the biggest form of contraception worldwide. The average woman who breastfeeds on an unrestricted basis whenever she or her baby wants, will not ovulate for fourteen months. This is why most women around the world have babies naturally spaced at about every two and a half years for much of their reproductive life.

The contraceptive prospect changed with the advent of the Pill, as women could now take total responsibility for their reproductive activity and men were excluded, except, of course, inasmuch as they took a part in the woman's decision. There are signs that couples today are making contraception a joint decision, but having said this young couples indulging in intercourse and ignoring contraception are still taking chances both by risking an unwanted pregnancy and by exposing themselves to the hazards of sexually transmitted diseases. Given that most people in their late teens feel indestructible and that, in their view, diseases and pregnancy are things that happen to someone else, there may be little that can be done to improve matters.

Young partners engaging in sex, as the vast majority do, tend to be somewhat impulsive in their choice of contraceptive, if indeed they use anything at all. This makes the condom (sheath) the most popular. As a couple settle down to a regular sex life together the Pill becomes the more common method. It has many advantages, as we shall see, and is used by many healthy young women until they start a family. It is a good idea to stop the Pill six months before trying for a baby, so that all your metabolic processes are back to normal before conception occurs.

Once a young couple have a family they might think again about the Pill and often tend to choose a barrier form of contraceptive, such as the diaphragm or cap, the sponge, or, of course, the condom. The intrauterine device, or IUD, has been a popular choice for women in the past, but questions are now being raised about the hazards of internal infections that can put future fertility at risk. As a result, some doctors, especially in the United States, are thinking twice before suggesting this as a contraceptive method to any couple who want to have babies in the future. There is now only one accepted IUD available in the United States, as a result of costly litigation against IUD manufacturers.

Used intelligently and meticulously, natural methods of contraception can be as effective as the diaphragm, when a space is desired before the next child. Whatever method a couple use to space their two or maybe three children, it is usually no great problem if conception occurs at some time other than the 'ideal' one they had set themselves. However, as the years pass and they complete their family, most couples now seek something more reliable to prevent further pregnancies. Such couples are not 'family planning' any more – they do not want more babies at all, as far as they can foretell.

This attitude has led to a situation in which some form of sterilization is the favoured contraception by about a third of all couples over thirty-eight years old. This is becoming more popular, as women become less happy about the long-term effects of the Pill, and even the mini-Pill, and are prepared to take the gamble that they will not change their minds about having more children. With so many divorces and remarriages nowadays, this can be a problem as some people find that they want to have a baby with a new partner, many years after they have been sterilized. Research into reliable, yet reversible, methods of sterilization has now become a real priority for the future.

Let us look now at each of the commonly used methods of contraception and see what their advantages and disadvantages are. We will also look at how they can be used lovingly as part of an active sex life.

Male methods are, as we have seen, the most popular worldwide. The most common by far is the condom, or sheath. This has received enormous publicity and increasing public acceptance because of its protective value against the transmission of the AIDS virus.

The advantages of the condom are that it is safe, cheap, can be used by any man, gives good protection against venereal diseases and AIDS in particular; reduces penile sensitivity which can help the man who ejaculates prematurely; can be used when the woman has a vaginal infection yet still wants sex; can be contoured and ribbed to produce extra and different sensations for the woman; is widely available without prescription or having to go to doctors or clinics; and has no medical side-effects.

There are only two possible disadvantages. Although the resulting reduction in sensitivity of the penis can suit some men, for others this is not an advantage. Some women also dislike the condom as it reduces stimulation for them. Thin condoms are better in this respect, but with AIDS protection in mind, condoms need to be thicker and tougher, which will increase this problem still further. The other disadvantage that couples complain of is that because using a condom is directly related to the sexual act, donning it can interrupt the flow

of lovemaking at a critical moment. This need not necessarily be a problem, because many loving couples find that they get considerable pleasure from the woman putting the sheath on to her man as a part of foreplay, and this is what I recommend.

For a condom to be effective and pleasant to wear it must be properly used. Firstly, never re-use a condom. Next, ensure that you put it on well before the penis comes near the vaginal area. There can be sperms in the fluid that a man leaks from his penis, even before he ejaculates. When the penis is fully erect, take the tip of the condom between the finger and thumb of one hand, and use the fingers of the other hand to roll the rubber down, so that the penis is completely covered. Excluding the air from the teat of the tip of the condom in this way enables it to be filled with semen when the man ejaculates.

When the sheath is applied you should be able to see the packing rings clearly. Now have sex as you normally would and after ejaculation, and before the erection subsides, the penis should be withdrawn, holding the base of the condom at the same time, to be sure that it does not come off inside the vagina.

To be really safe from both pregnancy and the risk of sexually transmitted disease it makes sense to use a spermicidal jelly or foam in the vagina. This kills the AIDS virus and adds to contraceptive safety. Never use Vaseline or any other greasy or petroleum-based lubricant. Use only water-based lubricants because they do not perish the rubber of the sheath.

From a lovemaking point of view or if you use fun condoms as sex aids, the condom can be highly successful if both of you make the most of putting it on. Some women are happy to fellate their man only if he wears a sheath whilst others find the taste of the rubber in their mouth unacceptable – although there are now flavoured ones available! My clinical experience has taught me that most couples prefer not to use a condom if they do not have to, but that of all the methods available it is still a favourite in many sexual situations.

The male Pill has been much talked about but is still far from becoming a reality. From a legal point of view, pharmaceutical companies are likely to be increasingly wary of manufacturing such a Pill, until any possibility of harmful side effects has been eliminated. One of the world's leading experts has said that given the current state of litigation over contraceptive side effects, there is little doubt that we shall end the century with fewer rather than more methods of contraception than when we started.

Even if a male Pill could be perfected, and this is possible, many women tell me that they would not trust their men to take it reliably. After all, they claim, it is the woman who must carry the baby if the man has been less than responsible, and, of course, they are right. It makes sense to me that a man is less likely to be scrupulous about taking such a Pill given that it is not he who personally stands to gain the greatest benefit from doing so. This must, in my view, lead to method failure. I do not therefore envisage the male Pill becoming widely available for mass use in the foreseeable future.

She has applied a condom as a part of their foreplay together. Neither partner feels that their lovemaking has been interrupted.

Vasectomy is a simple procedure in which the sperm-carrying ducts are tied off and cut so that sperms can no longer travel to the penis. It must be treated as irreversible for all practical purposes even though some men do have successful reversal operations. The advantages are that as a contraceptive method it is virtually one hundred per cent effective; it does not affect sex drive in most men; once done it requires no further thought; and the man can be sure that he does not father any children he does not want.

The major disadvantage with vasectomy is that it should be thought of as virtually irreversible which can be a heartache for the remarried man who wants children with his new wife. Reversal rates at operation are increasing as expertise is gained by the medical profession. Some studies show that in highly skilled hands, well over half of all operations can now be reversed. Another potential disadvantage is that in the psychosexually unstable man who has sexual problems he may not even be conscious of, it can trigger off further sexual performance difficulties. Lastly, a vasectomy is not immediately effective, and other contraceptive methods have to be used for about four months after the operation until the system is cleared of live sperms. This can be a tricky time for some couples if the woman is at all uncertain or uneasy about her man being sterilized, and tries to achieve a pregnancy one last time.

From a sexual point of view, vasectomy is the ideal choice for most couples. It enables spontaneous, uninterrupted sex and poses no great medical hazards. This freedom from worry about contraception can often open up a whole new chapter in a couple's sexual life together.

Coitus interruptus, or withdrawal, is an age-old but somewhat unsatisfactory contraceptive method in which the man removes his penis from the vagina just before he ejaculates. The failure rate is very high and lovemaking can be unrewarding, as the couple have to adopt a very restricted number of positions if the man is to have any real chance of withdrawing quickly enough; the woman often feels that she cannot truly relax because she is so apprehensive that he will ejaculate inside her and make her pregnant; and few, if any, women have orgasms with such minimal thrusting. Lastly, it is a poor method for less mature couples because the man may not have learned to anticipate his orgasm, and so will be less able to withdraw in time. Having said this, some couples who are very experienced with one another and where the man has near perfect ejaculatory control, can use this method with ease.

Of the female methods of contraception, of which there are many more than male, the best known is the combined contraceptive Pill. This works by suppressing ovulation with hormones. When the woman stops taking it, after either twenty-one or -two days, she experiences a withdrawal bleed which appears to be a period. The other type of Pill is the mini-Pill that is taken all month round. This is more suitable for older women for whom the combined Pill might be considered too dangerous on health grounds.

The major advantage of the Pill is that it is one hundred per cent effective if taken on time every day. It is not directly linked to intercourse and a woman is free to have sex whenever she likes, without preparation. It does not intrude on lovemaking at all. The Pill also has some medical effects that are positive. For example, certain diseases of the breast, cancer of the ovary, cancer of the womb lining, and rheumatoid arthritis are less common in women taking the Pill. Some women report a better complexion, especially just before a period when it is most often at its worst. The Pill also enables a woman to plan her periods so that she is not menstruating on holiday or on her honeymoon, for example. This can be done by taking two full packs one after the other without a break and can only be employed if one is taking a combined contraceptive Pill. Newer, so-called 'tri-phasic' Pills can be juggled so as to postpone a period but it is much more complicated and must be discussed with your doctor. Women on the Pill have fewer period pains and they are less painful when they do occur. The actual blood loss is less both in amount and duration in a Pill-induced period because there is less build-up of womb lining.

This formidable list of advantages has made the contraceptive Pill the most popular choice for most young women who are fit and healthy. It provides women with complete sexual freedom and total responsibility for their fertility.

Against this the Pill is receiving an increasingly bad press in various health areas and there is little doubt, in my view, that fewer women will be prepared to take it as the years go by. Working from research done using the older style, high-dose combined contraceptive Pills, doctors still act cautiously when suggesting a Pill for older women. This is because it was found that women over thirty-five years old had increased risks of cardiovascular disease, strokes, and clots in their veins if they took the high-dose Pill. This was especially so if they also smoked and were overweight. Evidence linking the Pill to breast cancer and cancer of the cervix is conflicting. As experience with the newer, low-dose Pills, and more latterly the tri-phasic Pills accumulates, evidence about the adverse effects of the Pill may have to be reconsidered. In the meantime, doctors tend to recommend that an older woman use another form of contraception or a mini-Pill of the progestogen-only type.

The only other contraceptive method that could offer the same sort of cover without side effects is an anti-pregnancy vaccination which is currently under test in the United States. Research is also being carried out on a female condom that fits into the vagina and over the vulva. It is currently under test in various countries. It looks rather like a very wide male sheath that is sealed at one end. The closed end is put into the vagina where it is held in place with a ring. A ring at the open end keeps this from slipping into the vagina. Men involved in the tests say that they find it preferable to a male condom and some women claim that it improves orgasm, perhaps because the outer ring rubs the clitoris.

The IUD, or coil, has been a favourite method of contraception for women over many years, mainly because once in place in the cavity of the uterus, it can be left there and forgotten for a long time. It does not interfere with lovemaking and does suit some women well. It is not known how an IUD works but somehow its presence in the womb prevents a fertilized egg from embedding and developing into a foetus. It is unobtrusive during lovemaking but some men say that they can feel the 'tail' of the device that is left protruding from the woman's cervix so that the IUD can be removed at a later date. If this is a problem it can usually be cut shorter by a doctor.

However, using the IUD many women experience heavier periods; the device can be expelled without the woman knowing it; the long-term effects of irritating the uterus are not known; pregnancies occurring outside the womb and in the fallopian tubes are more common in IUD users; it has to be inserted by an expert in the first place; and last, but by no means least, IUDs are known to cause infections of the uterus and fallopian tubes. These infections are usually not obvious clinically yet may render the woman sterile. As I mentioned earlier in this section, this has led some cautious doctors to be reluctant to prescribe the coil for any woman who might want to have more children.

Vaginal spermicide tablets, foams and jellies are useful, but not on their own. They must be put into the vagina before sex and should be used with a condom or diaphragm. They are easy to use, inexpensive, and work well. But many women find them messy and they do not enhance oral sex. It is also advisable not to wash or bathe for six hours after to ensure complete cover.

In my opinion, the diaphragm or cap is a grossly underrated contraceptive method. It is easy to use; inexpensive; only used when the woman wants to have sex; has no side effects; can be nearly as effective as the Pill; and can be used to hold back menstrual flow for the couple who like to have sex during her menstrual period. The disadvantages of the cap are that it does not suit the woman who has reservations about handling her genitals; it interferes with the sensations in the front wall of the vagina (around the G-spot) which can be a nuisance for the woman who enjoys this stimulation; it has to be put in before sex and so requires some forethought; and it must be checked regularly as it can develop holes. In spite of these disadvantages, the diaphragm is a good contraceptive method for the couple who are spacing their family, and even for the woman who has completed her childbearing and is perhaps less fertile than she used to be in her twenties.

The loving couple who use a diaphragm can easily make inserting it a part of foreplay, and in the early days of learning to use it, much fun can be had chasing it, as it slips out of your fingers across the bed! Women with an active sex life regularly put their cap in every night when they clean their teeth, and then do not have to worry whether or not they have sex. Alternatively, if you are likely to have sex only rarely, the diaphragm is a very good contraceptive method because it is directly linked to the act itself, and means you do not have anything in or on your body between sexual episodes.

The sponge is a disc of material impregnated with spermicide that is put into the vagina much like the diaphragm. It can be bought over the counter at chemist shops and drugstores, is easy to use and works well for most women. Recent studies show a ninety-four per cent success rate, which means that for the woman who is perhaps outside her most fertile period of life or who is trying to space her family and does not mind a 'failure', it is perfect. It is however, fairly expensive and can only be used once. Sexually, it provides few problems, other than to the couple who dislikes the feel of the sponge, either in the vagina, or against the penis or their fingers. Again, as with the diaphragm, putting it in can become a sport in itself.

There are several natural methods of birth control that involve the detailed monitoring of ovulation by studying the woman's vaginal mucus, her temperature, or both. Once learned, these methods are easy to perform, and can be very reliable if the couple is meticulous about using them. The best advantages in my view, derive from the formidable level of awareness such couples develop about the woman's sexual cycle. Really able couples can tell just by feeling the woman's cervix, exactly where she is in her cycle, and thus her fertility. Others become adept at mucus diagnosis. This knowledge helps the man to become aware of his partner's physical body far better than any other method, and most couples find that this in itself makes for greater togetherness and understanding. It also encourages other methods of lovemaking during the most fertile days of the month, when true intercourse would probably result in pregnancy. This calls for ingenuity and creativity in lovemaking which must certainly reduce the possibility of sexual boredom!

Sterilization, in a woman, should be treated as a virtually irreversible procedure in which the fallopian tubes are cut and tied, or clipped, so that eggs cannot travel to the uterus and sperms cannot travel up to fertilize an egg. A woman who has had her tubes tied is one hundred per cent safe contracep tively, and apart from some changes in the nature of menstruation in a few women, there are no notable side effects. The freedom that sterilization gives to the average couple more than outweighs any disadvantages and the vast majority of women and their partners are happy with the procedure. As with male sterilization, it frees the couple for sex at any time, anywhere, which can bring new levels of sexual spontaneity.

Whilst contraception is, of course, a subject of concern to anyone who is sexually active it is especially important to the unmarried, and particularly young people. Teens and early twenties are a time for sexual exploration in the search for a partner but perhaps especially today, many young people are concerned about their sexual health and that of their partners'. Given that it is impossible to be sure of anyone's sexual suitability from the point of view of AIDS or other sexually transmitted diseases, it is almost certainly best to play safe and use a condom on every occasion, even if you are using another method as well. This also applies to older people who are having sex with partners of whom they cannot be sure. Most research still shows that young people are foolhardy about carrying and using condoms but perhaps as they become more fashionable and with women increasingly taking the initiative this attitude will change.

Generally, contraception has been concerned with preventing unwanted pregnancies and many people have lost sight of the fact that the older methods, such as the condom, were originally used as protectives against venereal diseases. Sexually transmitted diseases are even more common today and any thoughtful couple, unless they are very sure of one another's genital health and fidelity, would be wise to consider protecting themselves not only against pregnancy, but also against AIDS, and other sexually transmitted diseases. This means that the condom will continue to increase in popularity as a contraceptive method because it is the only one that deals with both 'hazards'. No other method of contraception protects against sexually transmitted diseases. For the couple who are sure of one another, however, there is a bigger choice of contraceptive methods. Just how much bigger this choice will be as a result of future research is anyone's guess, but in my opinion, we are going to stay with the methods currently available for some time to come.

CASEBOOK

*As an 'Agony Uncle' I have received an increasing number of letters
asking specific questions related to the AIDS virus. Other
common worries and concerns are also included here.*

I am terribly worried about AIDS. Can I catch it from kissing my boyfriend?
No one knows for sure but current research suggests that you cannot contract
AIDS from kissing your partner's mouth. I am sure, however, that it is unwise to
kiss or suck a man's penis unless you can be totally certain of his sexual
history. It is now thought to be unwise to brush your teeth before oral sex.
because by doing so you can cause small lacerations of the gums through
which the AIDS virus could travel if the man or woman is affected.

*My husband will not use a vibrator inside me because he says that I might
become addicted to it and go off him. Does this ever occur?*
It sounds to me that he has something of an inferiority complex about his
ability to satisfy you. Most women who use a vibrator do not become addicted
to the sensations it produces, even if they use it regularly. A vibrator does,
however, produce reliable and highly arousing sensations for many women.
The best way to overcome your problem with your husband is to involve him
with your toy and to school him in using it to delight you.

*I really like anal sex with my partner whom I have known for seven years. She is
worried about AIDS but we are both faithful and I say there is no problem. What
do you think?*
You are right. There is no problem if you are both faithful to each other. Anal
sex has been a favourite since time immemorial, and it is a shame that today
many couples are missing out on an enjoyable part of their repertoire because
they believe that anal sex itself somehow *causes* AIDS. This is not so. It is a
dangerous practise if either of you has any sort of sexually transmitted disease
and especially, of course, if you are HIV-positive. Otherwise, it should continue
to be a pleasant part of your love life.

*My girlfriend has gigantic orgasms when I caress her G-spot and also seems to
spurt out some fluid. What is happening?*
Some women actually ejaculate fluid from their urinary passage as they
climax. This is more likely to occur if they are stimulating their G-spot. The
subject has been debated for many years, but there is now little doubt that
female ejaculation is a fact. It has been studied under laboratory conditions
and the fluid is definitely not urine. It is much more like male prostatic
secretions and is almost certainly produced by the little glands along the walls
of the urinary passage. Given that this is the area caressed when you stroke her
G-spot, it is hardly surprising that you notice it most then. It is not a problem
and therefore should not cause you anxiety.

We play all kinds of games putting things in my wife's vagina. Is this safe?
Yes it is, provided that you never use anything that could break. Preferably use things that were made to be put there. Professionally manufactured sex toys are safe if they are kept clean but beware of home-made versions. Many couples experiment with foods such as slices of mango or banana and this can be delicious. Beware though of sugary foods such as jam and sweets because sometimes any remaining material can alter the environment inside the vagina and cause an infection. Always wash or douche the vagina afterwards.

My husband has heard that it is nice to have his prostate gland stimulated. How do I do this and is it safe?
Much has been written about the G-spot for women but many men say that they too obtain great pleasure from their G-spot being caressed. This area is found a couple of inches inside his anus on the front wall of the back passage. The prostate gland lies here and can be easily reached with the man lying on his back with his legs drawn up.

When stimulating a man's G-spot be sure to go gently at first. Lubricate your finger well and if you are at all concerned use a plastic, disposable glove or finger stall. Gently insert one finger first and as he relaxes, seek the best area to stroke. A sort of 'come here' movement with the finger, or even two fingers, is usually best. According to several studies, those men who like this sort of stimulation say that they obtain their 'best ever' orgasms if their penis is caressed at the same time.

After such an anal caress be sure to wash your fingers well before putting them anywhere near your vagina.

My girlfriend likes me to put several fingers in her vagina as she gets excited. What could I do when they are inside her to give her a real thrill?
Women vary a lot as to what they best like when it comes to fingers inside them. For some, a single finger held quite still is best, but most say that they like their vagina to be stretched widely as they reach climax. Any woman who has had a baby can take three fingers once she is aroused, and a few women like even more.

Once your fingers are inside, you can move them around or in and out as if they were a penis, and you can experiment with caressing her cervix deep inside. This knob-like protrusion can be easily felt, especially if she draws her legs back to her chest or if she is on all-fours. For some women the sensations produced by cervical caresses are exquisite and can bring them to orgasm even if nothing else is done. Others complain of pain if their cervix is even touched. Only experience will tell you what is best for your partner.

I really like my boyfriend to squeeze my nipples very hard as I climax. Am I odd or is this normal?
You are probably perfectly normal. Many women enjoy very firm nipple pressure and a few even want some pain as they climax. Most men tend to be too gentle at such times and the secret is for you to guide him as to when and how the pressure should be applied.

CHAPTER SIX

MAKING LOVE
WITH
INTERCOURSE

For most people 'making love' is synonymous with intercourse and however much they enjoy other sexual activities, intercourse still seems to many people to be the most natural progression from mutual pleasuring. It is the highest form of physical and even spiritual communication between a man and a woman, and has the power to transform a relationship into something that both partners cherish and value.

LOVEMAKING POSITIONS

*Most of us begin our sexual lives quite modestly, but with time,
care, a little effort and some real communication, we can
transform this rather simple, biological activity into a supreme
piece of communication and sharing.*

Any reader who has come this far with me, will know that intercourse
is not the start of a journey into a couples's sexual relationship, but the
consummation of a lovemaking partnership. This is not a sex book as such,
and there are many books that give much more detail about actual intercourse
than I will now offer, but for the sake of completeness, and for the couple who
are sure of one another's sexual health and faithfulness and who *will* want to
bring their lovemaking to the final stage of commitment, this short section
represents an introduction.

Any man and woman can have sex, as such. This physical coupling that
occurs between a man and a woman can be achieved quite quickly and
mechanically. The reader of this book though, is unlikely to find this the
rewarding experience I have just outlined. So what does make for true loving
intercourse, as opposed to hasty copulation?

Intercourse is probably the most profound communication possible between
a man and a woman. It is true 'making love'. Everything in intercourse is
personalized to one's partner; it is partner-centred; involves absolute commitment; is an integral part of a couple's life style; treats the partner's needs as
central; calls for insight and imagination; improves with time; improves the
value of our partner; can be varied according to needs of the time; knows no
barriers; adapts to occasional failure; ensures 'inter-personal' communication;
positively encourages improvement; and is a lifetime's investment.

Set against this inspiring background, lovemaking positions become almost
insignificant. Indeed, although the sex gurus of the 1960s and 1970s made
much of lovemaking positions and many books have chronicled them in detail,
the majority of couples find that they use only three or four positions
throughout a whole sexual lifetime. Problems can arise if one or the other
becomes bored by the same position year in, year out, but any couple that can
talk things over usually find that they can deal with this.

All change is to some extent threatening, as we have seen throughout the
book, and changing from a familiar lovemaking position can appear daunting.
Many, women especially, find that they have inhibitions about adopting
positions that they fear may somehow be shameful, or less than flattering.
There are many women who see any position other than the straight
missionary one as being somehow not natural, or 'perverted'. If this is a
problem for you, then it might be that you will need to talk things over with a
professional or perhaps your partner.

At first sight, it might appear that intercourse is merely the placing of a penis
into a vagina. Indeed, for some couples this is all it does mean. However, true

lovemaking involves far more than this and can give pleasure at a level that transcends anything else a couple do together.

The angle at which the penis enters the woman can greatly affect the sensations for both partners. By altering your positions it is possible to make the penis come into contact with almost anywhere in the woman's pelvis. The more the woman's legs are drawn back to her chest the deeper the penetration, but this might be painful or uncomfortable at various times within her menstrual cycle. Some women tell me that they receive the best sensations from extremely deep penetration – indeed, many say that in a symbolic way, they feel most 'female' and receiving when penetrated deeply. Other women enjoy shallow penetration with their legs almost in line with their bodies.

Positions where the woman is on all-fours permit the penis to stimulate the front vaginal wall, where the woman's G-spot is located. For some women this is the only way that they can have an orgasm during intercourse.

Couples who gain the most pleasure from intercourse move their bodies continually as they subtly alter their positions to give and receive the best sensations. But this movement is not limited to whole body changes of position. Both partners can also move their genitals in highly arousing ways. If you are a woman you can contract and relax your pelvic floor muscles, so that you grip your partner's penis and release it rhythmically as he thrusts. And for a man not only is thrusting highly stimulating for himself and his partner but he can keep the penis still and, by contracting *his* pelvic muscles, 'twitch' the head of the penis in a teasing way inside the vagina.

Many possible combinations of fast, slow, regular and irregular rhythms are possible during lovemaking. An exquisite Chinese method requires the man to thrust nine times in a very shallow way at the vaginal entrance, and then on the tenth thrust to push the penis deep inside. Repeating the combination of teasing yet rhythmical play at the entrance and the inevitability of the final, tenth deep penetration can be immensely satisfying for a woman.

The creative couple pleases one another in all kinds of ways at the same time that actual intercourse is taking place. This means looking at any lovemaking positions you are thinking of using with a view to adding extra delights by way of enhancement. Some of the things worth considering are: Can the woman move easily? Is the position good for deep penetration? Is it good for shallow penetration? Could it be comfortable during pregnancy? Can the man reach his partner's breasts? Can he caress her clitoris easily? Can he see her vulva? Can she hold his scrotum or stroke his penis? Does the penis stimulate the front vaginal wall around the G-spot? Can you both kiss? How good is it for cuddling one another? How tiring will it be? What freedom of movement does it permit both partners?

A good way to embark upon more adventurous lovemaking activities is to share with each other what it is that either one or both of you would like to initiate or experience as part of the intercourse that you are currently enjoying. Then think about what basic things, such as those listed above, you want to make happen. You will soon be able to work out the best positions.

Let us look now at a few lovemaking positions that are proven favourites with lovers the world over.

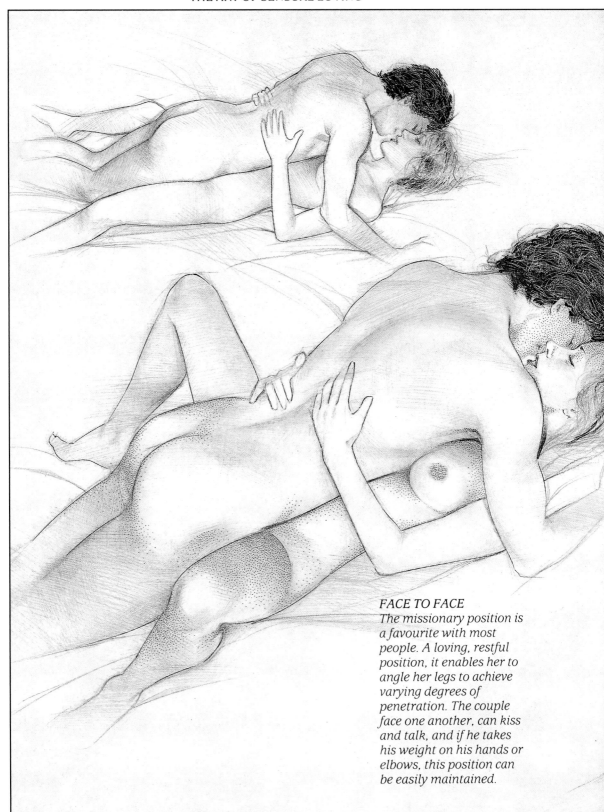

FACE TO FACE
The missionary position is a favourite with most people. A loving, restful position, it enables her to angle her legs to achieve varying degrees of penetration. The couple face one another, can kiss and talk, and if he takes his weight on his hands or elbows, this position can be easily maintained.

FACE TO FACE
With her legs over his shoulders, penetration is extremely deep. This is very arousing for him, and she will enjoy the sensation of his penis caressing her cervix. A pillow under her bottom can help to make her more comfortable. This is an exceptionally good position for the couple who are trying for a baby.

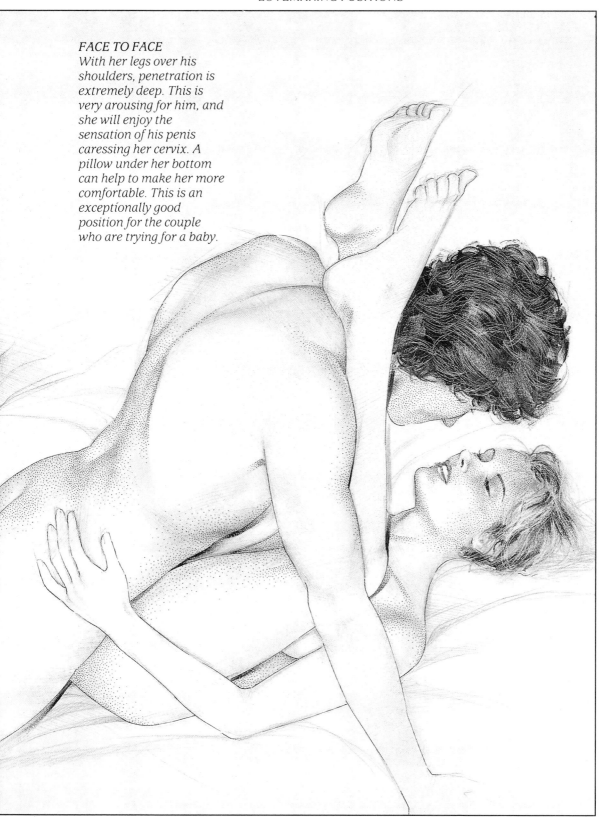

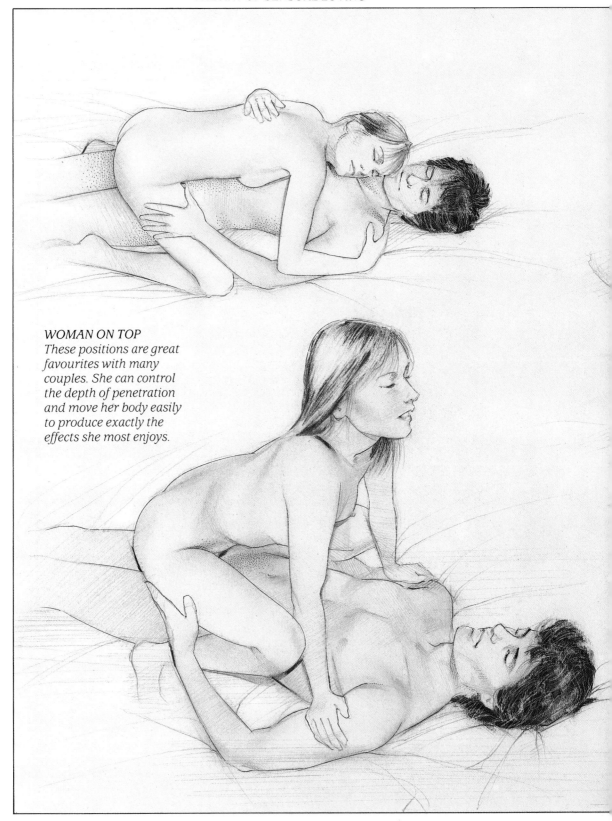

WOMAN ON TOP
These positions are great favourites with many couples. She can control the depth of penetration and move her body easily to produce exactly the effects she most enjoys.

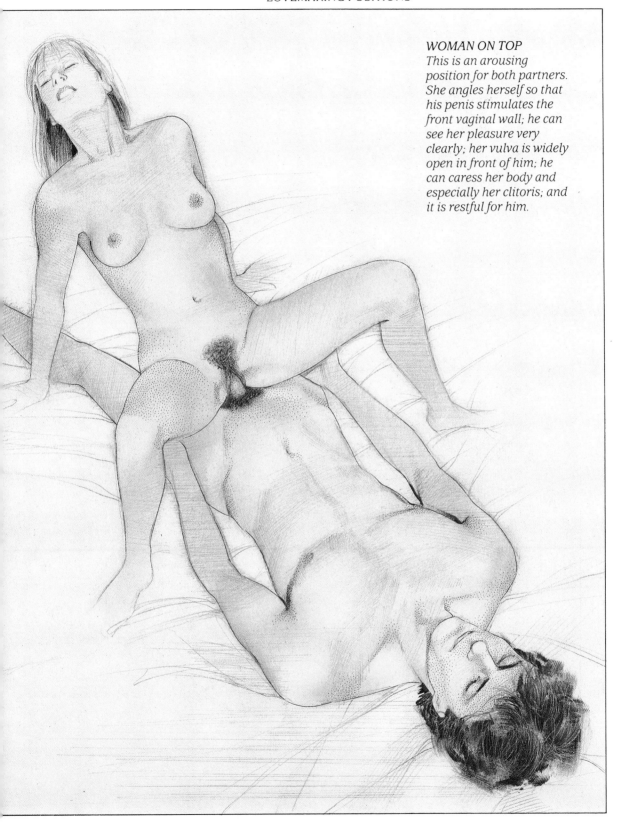

WOMAN ON TOP
This is an arousing
position for both partners.
She angles herself so that
his penis stimulates the
front vaginal wall; he can
see her pleasure very
clearly; her vulva is widely
open in front of him; he
can caress her body and
especially her clitoris; and
it is restful for him.

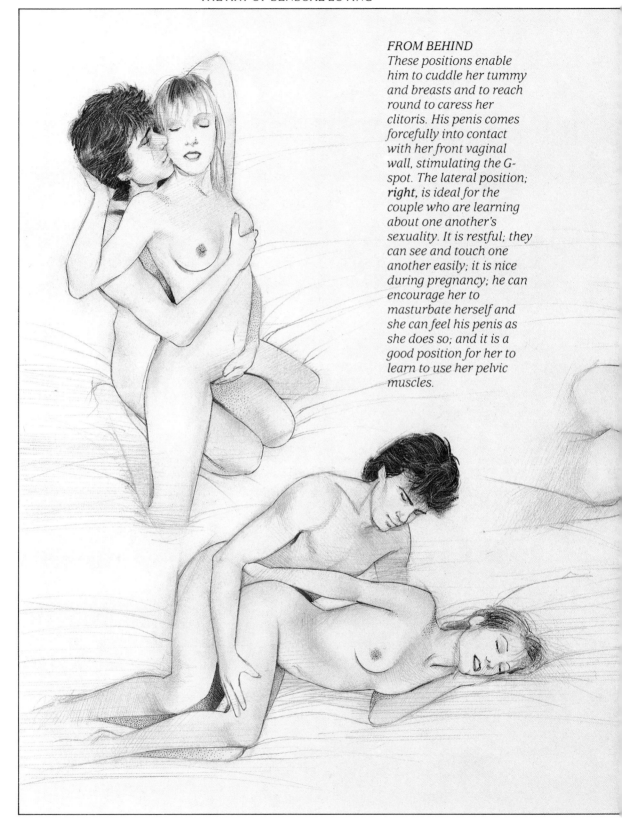

FROM BEHIND
*These positions enable
him to cuddle her tummy
and breasts and to reach
round to caress her
clitoris. His penis comes
forcefully into contact
with her front vaginal
wall, stimulating the G-
spot. The lateral position;
right, is ideal for the
couple who are learning
about one another's
sexuality. It is restful; they
can see and touch one
another easily; it is nice
during pregnancy; he can
encourage her to
masturbate herself and
she can feel his penis as
she does so; and it is a
good position for her to
learn to use her pelvic
muscles.*

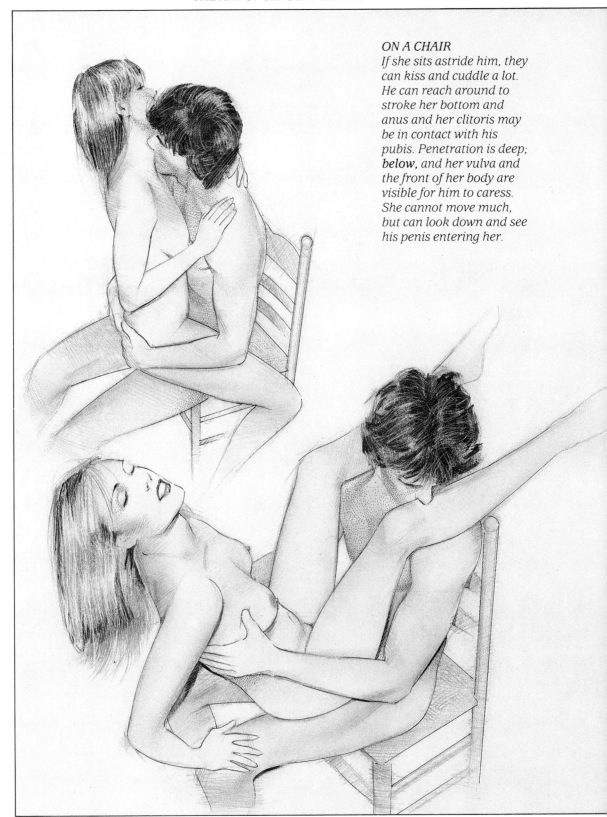

ON A CHAIR
*If she sits astride him, they
can kiss and cuddle a lot.
He can reach around to
stroke her bottom and
anus and her clitoris may
be in contact with his
pubis. Penetration is deep;
below, and her vulva and
the front of her body are
visible for him to caress.
She cannot move much,
but can look down and see
his penis entering her.*

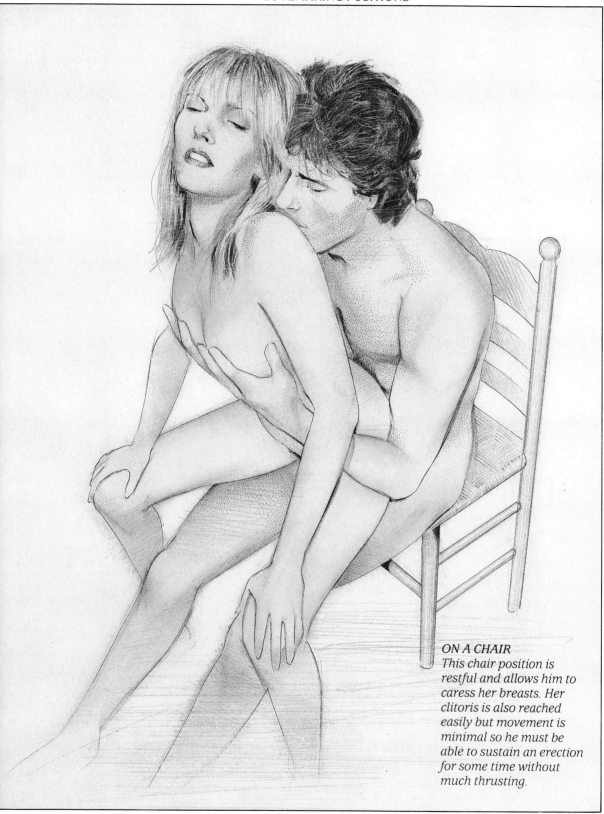

ON A CHAIR
This chair position is restful and allows him to caress her breasts. Her clitoris is also reached easily but movement is minimal so he must be able to sustain an erection for some time without much thrusting.

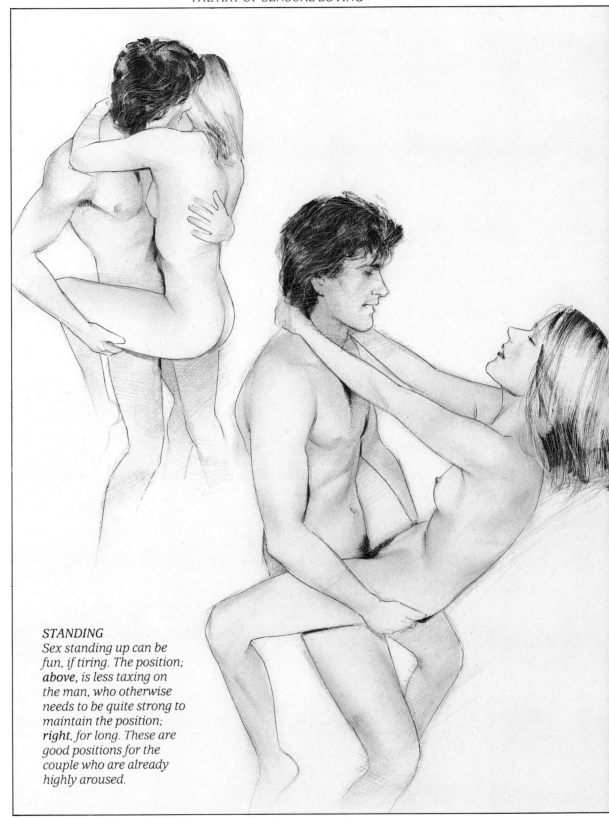

STANDING

Sex standing up can be fun, if tiring. The position; **above,** is less taxing on the man, who otherwise needs to be quite strong to maintain the position; **right,** for long. These are good positions for the couple who are already highly aroused.

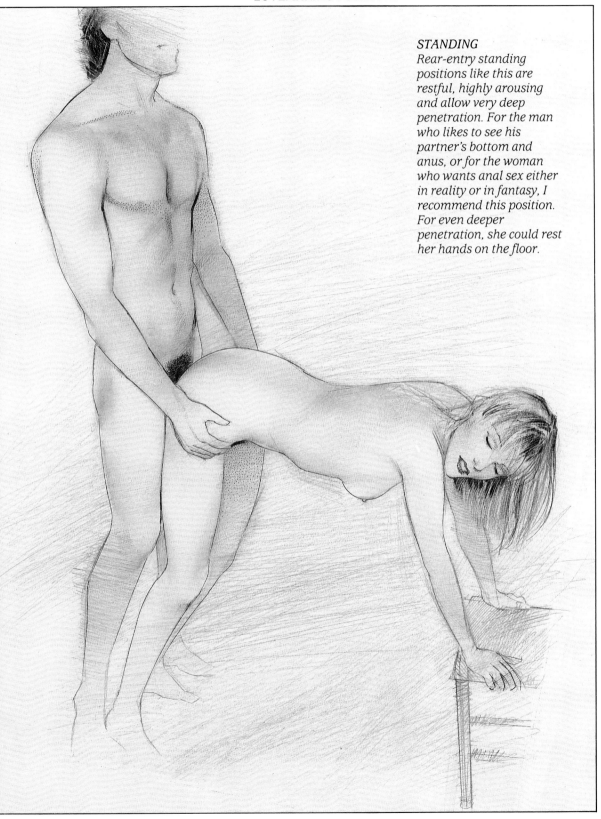

STANDING
Rear-entry standing positions like this are restful, highly arousing and allow very deep penetration. For the man who likes to see his partner's bottom and anus, or for the woman who wants anal sex either in reality or in fantasy, I recommend this position. For even deeper penetration, she could rest her hands on the floor.

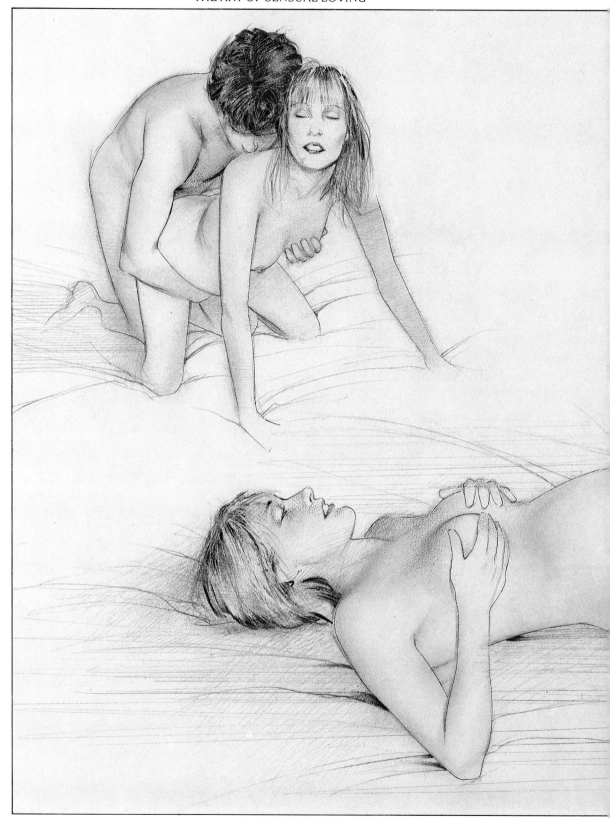

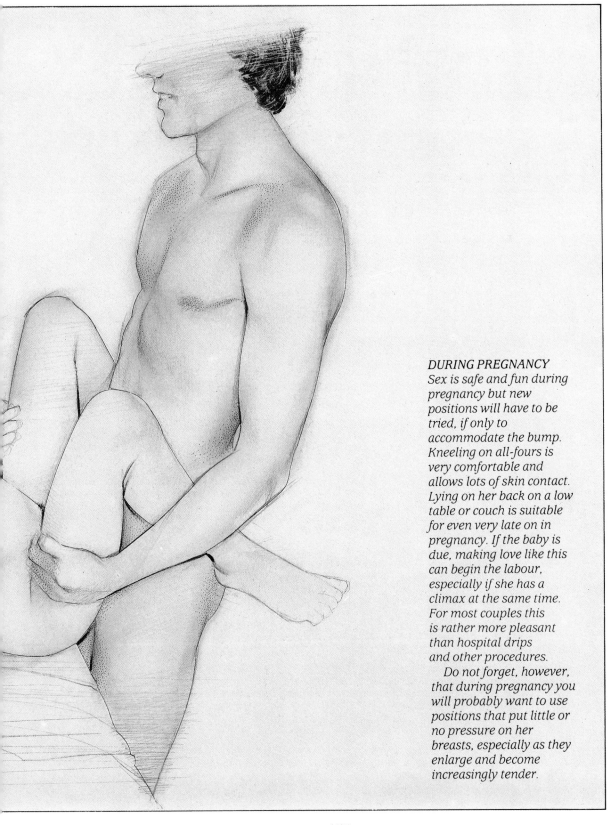

DURING PREGNANCY
Sex is safe and fun during pregnancy but new positions will have to be tried, if only to accommodate the bump. Kneeling on all-fours is very comfortable and allows lots of skin contact. Lying on her back on a low table or couch is suitable for even very late on in pregnancy. If the baby is due, making love like this can begin the labour, especially if she has a climax at the same time. For most couples this is rather more pleasant than hospital drips and other procedures.

Do not forget, however, that during pregnancy you will probably want to use positions that put little or no pressure on her breasts, especially as they enlarge and become increasingly tender.

FURTHER READING

A selection of some books that make a particular contribution to the literature in this area that readers will find illuminating and provocative.

The Art of Intimacy, P. and T. Malone, New York, Simon & Schuster, 1987

The Art of Loving, Erich Fromm, New York, Harper & Row, 1974

Becoming Orgasmic: A Sexual Growth Programme for Women, J. Heiman and J. LoPiccola, New Jersey, Prentice Hall, 1977

The Family Book about Sexuality, Mary Calderone and Eric Johnson, New York, Bantam Books, 1983

Female Sexual Awareness, Barry and Emily McCarthy, New York, Carroll & Graf, 1989

The Hite Report on Male Sexuality, Shere Hite, New York, Alfred A. Knopf, 1981

The Joy of Sex, A. Comfort, New York, Crown, 1986

Kiss Sleeping Beauty Goodbye, M. Kolbenschlag, New York, Bantam Books, 1984

Male Sexual Awareness, Barry McCarthy, New York, Carroll & Graf, 1984

The New Bodies, Ourselves: A Book by and for Women, Boston Women's Health Book Collective, New York, Simon & Schuster, 1984

Sex, the Facts, the Acts and Your Feelings, Michael Carrerra, New York, Crown, 1981

Sexual Awareness, Barry and Emily McCarthy, New York, Carroll & Graf, 1984

Sexual Exercises for Women, A. Harris, New York, Carroll & Graf, 1988

Touching: The Human Significance of the Skin, A. Montagu, New York, Harper & Row, 1986

A Woman's Guide to Men & Sex, Andrew Stanway, New York, Carroll & Graf, 1988

INDEX

Thanks to my darling wife Penny
who has made it possible and enjoyable for me
to practise what I preach.